QUALITATIVE CHEMICAL ANALYSIS

ARTHUR A. NOYES

THE MACMILLAN COMPANY
NEW YORK · BOSTON · CHICAGO · DALLAS
ATLANTA · SAN FRANCISCO

MACMILLAN & CO., Limited
LONDON · BOMBAY · CALCUTTA
MELBOURNE

**THE MACMILLAN COMPANY
OF CANADA, Limited**
TORONTO

A COURSE OF INSTRUCTION

IN THE

QUALITATIVE
CHEMICAL ANALYSIS

OF INORGANIC SUBSTANCES

BY

ARTHUR A. NOYES

DIRECTOR OF THE GATES CHEMICAL LABORATORY,
CALIFORNIA INSTITUTE OF TECHNOLOGY

NINTH EDITION

New York
THE MACMILLAN COMPANY
1930

PREFACE

THIS text-book is an attempt, on the experimental side, to train the student of qualitative analysis in careful manipulation and exact methods of procedure, such as are commonly employed in quantitative analysis. It is an attempt, on the theoretical side, to make clear to the student the reason for each operation and result, and to accustom him to apply to them the laws of chemical equilibrium, and especially the principles relating to solubility and to the ionization, complex-formation, and oxidation and reduction of substances in solution. It is believed that in both these ways the educational value of the subject is greatly increased.

The book is divided into two main Parts, entitled The Course of Instruction and The System of Analysis. In presenting the System of Analysis the description of the operations is separated sharply from the discussion and explanation of them. The operations are described with as great definiteness as possible in short paragraphs entitled Procedures; and each of these is followed by Notes in which are given the reasons for the operations, the precautions necessary and difficulties encountered in special cases, the chemical behavior of the different constituents, the indications afforded of their presence, and the application of the theoretical principles to the reactions involved.

This System of Analysis is the result of many years' researches, during which the goal striven for has been gradually approached in the way illustrated by the successive editions of this book. This goal, by no means yet fully attained, has been the development of the simplest possible methods that will provide for the reliable detection of a small quantity (1 mg.) of any constituent in the presence of a large quantity (500 mg.) of any other constituent. The effort has also been made to avoid the use of tests, such as oversensitive color reactions, flame colorations, and bead tests, that do not enable the amounts of the various constituents present to be approximately estimated; for a satisfactory scheme of qualitative analysis carefully executed can be made to furnish this important information, thus often making unnecessary a more laborious quantitative analysis.

In the researches by which the System of Analysis has been brought into its present form, the author has had the able coöperation of many of his associates at the Massachusetts Institute of Technology and the California Institute of Technology. To Professors W. C. Bray and E. B. Spear belongs in largest measure the credit for the method of analysis of the aluminum and iron groups, to Professor W. C. Bray that for the alkaline-earth group, and to Professor Graham Edgar that for the detection of acidic constituents in non-igneous products as well as for improvements in many of the procedures of the copper and tin groups. The assistance and advice of Mr. Ernest H. Swift has been of great value in the final revision of the whole scheme of analysis. The author has also received many important suggestions from Professors Henry Fay, W. T. Hall, A. A. Blanchard, Edward Mueller, L. F. Hamilton, H. J. Lucas, and Mr. Roger Williams.

The Course of Instruction includes two sections — one entitled Laboratory Experiments, giving the directions for the laboratory work; and the other entitled Questions on the Experiments, consisting of a series of questions to be studied in connection with the class-room exercises.

The laboratory work described in the section on Laboratory Experiments is from beginning to end closely correlated with the systematic scheme of analysis. For experience has convinced the author that the plan followed in many text-books of requiring the student to study the separate reactions characteristic of the various elements before undertaking their systematic separation is highly unsatisfactory. However valuable the knowledge of the additional reactions might be, it is found in practice that the performance of so large a number of independent, disconnected experiments makes little impression on the student's mind and fails to awaken his interest in the subject. Qualitative analysis affords an effective means of teaching a part of inorganic chemistry chiefly because it unites into a connected whole a great variety of isolated facts, and because the student sees a practical use of the information presented to him; but these advantages evidently do not apply to facts not directly related to the process of analysis.

The Questions on the Experiments do not in general include such purely informational questions as are immediately suggested by the Notes on the Procedures. They are mainly intended to assist the instructor in training his students more fully in the general principles involved and in enabling them to derive from the subject the mental training it is capable of affording. They are in large part of such a character that, in order to answer them properly, the student must not only carefully study the Notes on the Procedures, but must also do independent thinking. It is assumed in these questions, as well as in the Notes on the Procedures, that the student has previously acquired, in his course on Inorganic Chemistry, a general knowledge of the mass-action law and of the chemical aspects of the ionic theory. To what extent the instructor will make use of the Questions will depend on the time available for the course and on the maturity of his students.

To make the course fully effective from an educational standpoint, it must be so conducted as to overcome the tendency of students to rush the laboratory experiments and to carry out the Procedures in a routine, unintelligent way. To this end the laboratory work must be supplemented by many class-room conferences with small sections of 15 to 25 students; thus there should be one such conference preceding every two laboratory exercises, or in the early stages of the course preceding each laboratory exercise, which should if possible be three hours long. The laboratory and class-room exercises should, moreover, be so correlated as to induct the student rather gradually into the detailed scheme of analysis of each group, but finally to secure by frequent repetition his full understanding of it. The best plan of doing this, in the author's opinion, involves four steps as follows: (1) Before beginning the laboratory work on any group the students are required to learn the outline of the process and the chemical reactions upon which it is mainly based, by studying the Table summarizing the analysis of that group and by reciting upon it in the class-room; but they should not be asked to learn in advance the details of the Procedures nor the contents of the Notes upon them. (2) The students then work through in the laboratory the Procedures of the group with a known solution (as described in the Laboratory Experiments), referring to the Notes, especially those with an experimental bearing. (3) They are then required to study the Notes more carefully, including those describing the principles involved, and (unless the course is a brief elementary one) to answer in writing, or prepare themselves to answer in the class-room, the corresponding Questions on the Experiments; all these matters being then taken up very fully in the class conferences, with the help of written tests, oral questioning, and explanations by the instructor. (4) After this full discussion the students review the group by analyzing in the laboratory one or more unknown solutions, as directed in the Laboratory Experiments.—In carrying out this plan it is desirable to keep the members of the class nearly together in their laboratory work, which may be accomplished by giving to the faster working students additional unknown solutions on each group, and by allowing those who are falling behind to omit some of the less important experiments, or to work overtime. In the laboratory great stress is laid on careful work, such as will enable the proportions of the various constituents present in unknown solutions to be estimated and small quantities of them to be detected. An effective means of teaching the details of manipulation, especially when the classes are large, is for the instructor to carry through in the lecture-room, after the students have had a little experience of their own in the laboratory, the complete process for the analysis of the copper-group.

Even when the time available for the subject of qualitative analysis does not permit of so complete a course as that here presented, the student gets, in the author's opinion, a better training by working through selected parts of an exact scheme of analysis carefully and thoroughly than he does by covering the whole of an elementary scheme superficially. Experiments that may be well omitted in briefer courses are indicated by asterisks prefixed to the description of them in the section entitled Laboratory Experiments.

PREFACE TO THE NINTH EDITION.

This edition differs from the preceding one mainly in that it includes a comprehensive index to the whole book, in which detailed references are made to all the procedures and notes. A number of changes suggested by further experience with the book have also been made in the text; and various errors have been corrected.

Pasadena, California, January, 1922.

CONTENTS

ix

TABLES OUTLINING THE SYSTEM OF ANALYSIS.

PART I
THE COURSE OF INSTRUCTION

LABORATORY EXPERIMENTS

GENERAL DIRECTIONS

Preliminary Work. — Check off on an apparatus list (corresponding to that printed in the Appendix) the apparatus found in the desk, and sign and hand in the list.

Make a 750 cc. wash-bottle, taking pains to bend the tubes and to cut them off so as to correspond closely with the model exhibited in the laboratory. Make also a 250 cc. wash-bottle (for washing with hot water and special solutions).

Make a dropper about 10 cm. (4 inches) long by drawing out one end of a glass tube to a fairly wide capillary and slightly expanding the other end with the aid of a file while it is heated in a flame. Cap the expanded end with a rubber nipple. Determine how many drops the dropper delivers to make 1 cc.; and, unless the number is within 3 or 4 of 30, widen or constrict the orifice till this is the case. Scratch on the dropper with a file a circle at the place where the volume is 1 cc.

Make 3 stirring-rods about 15 cm. long by cutting a piece of glass rod into sections and then rounding the ends in a flame.

Directions for Study. — Before carrying out each of the following experiments study the table (or other assignment) referred to at the beginning of the experiment. While making the experiment or after completing it, read the "Notes" referred to at the end of the experiment. After completing it, study the questions on it contained in the chapter entitled "Questions on the Experiments" (pages 19–38), writing out the answers to them or being prepared to recite upon them in the classroom, as the instructor may direct.

B

1

Directions as to the Note-book.—In the case of each of the experiments record in the note-book the operations very briefly; but record everything that happens fully, though concisely. Write equations expressing all the chemical changes that take place. In these equations represent solid substances by underlining their formulas, denote largely ionized dissolved substances by attaching to their formulas + and − signs in such a way as to show the ions into which they dissociate, and show slightly ionized dissolved substances by omitting these signs from their formulas. Thus the report on Expt. 1 would be made in the following form:

> **Expt. 1.** — Added HNO_3: no change observed.
> Added NH_4Cl: white curdy ppt.
> $$Ag^+NO_3^- + NH_4^+Cl^- = \underline{AgCl} + NH_4^+NO_3^-.$$
> Passed in H_2S: large black flocculent ppt.
> $$Cu^{++}(NO_3^-)_2 + H_2S = \underline{CuS} + 2\,H^+NO_3^-.$$

In regard to the solubility and ionization of substances, see the corresponding tables in the Appendix.

DETECTION OF THE BASIC CONSTITUENTS

Experiment 1. — *Separation of the Basic Constituents into Groups.* — Read the General Discussion on page 58, and study Table II (page 60). Measure out in a 10 cc. graduate 5 cc. portions of the test-solutions (see Note 1) of $AgNO_3$, $Cu(NO_3)_2$, $Zn(NO_3)_2$, $Ca(NO_3)_2$, and KNO_3. Mix the portions in a conical flask, add 5 cc. of 6 n. (6 normal) HNO_3 and 4 cc. of 3 n. NH_4Cl solution, shake the mixture for a minute or two, and filter it. Dilute the filtrate with water (see Note 2) to a volume of 100 cc. Pour it into a 200 cc. conical flask; insert a two-hole rubber stopper through which passes a tube leading to the bottom of the flask; and pass in through a gas-wash-bottle a moderate current of H_2S, till, upon closing the open hole in the stopper with the finger or with a piece of glass rod, the gas no longer bubbles through the wash-bottle. Filter the mixture. To the filtrate add 10 cc. of NH_4OH and 3 cc. of 6 n. $(NH_4)_2S$ solution. Shake the mixture and filter it. Evaporate the filtrate to a volume of about 10cc., filter, and to the cold solution add 5 cc. of $(NH_4)_2CO_3$ reagent and 5 cc. of ethyl alcohol.

Notes. — 1. The solutions of constituents to be tested for, here called the test-solutions, are all so made up as to contain 10 mg. (10 milligrams) of the constituent per cubic centimeter of solution. The mixture used in this experiment therefore contains 50 mg. of each of the basic constituents silver, copper, zinc, calcium, and potassium. The student should acquire the habit of working with definite quantities of the constituents and of noting the size of the precipitates which they yield. For a good qualitative analysis should not only show the presence or absence of the various constituents, but should also furnish an estimate of the proportions in which they are present.

Test-solutions should not be used in place of reagents, nor reagents in place of test-solutions, since the concentrations are, as a rule, quite different. Unless otherwise specified, all salt solutions used as reagents are 1 normal, and all acid or base solutions are 6 normal. The significance of the term *normal* is explained in Note 4, P. 11.

2. Distilled water should always be employed in qualitative analysis, and this is to be understood when water is mentioned.

Experiment 2. — *Precipitation of the Silver-Group. Principles Relating to Equivalents, Concentration, and Solubility-Effect.* — Study P. 11 (Procedure 11 of the System of Analysis) and the Notes on it.

Prepare about 20 cc. of a 3 n. NH_4Cl solution, describing in the note-book just how it is done.

Pour into a test-tube just 10 cc. of the test-solution of $Pb(NO_3)_2$, and add from a dropper the 3 n. NH_4Cl solution, 3 drops at a time, till after shaking a precipitate remains. Calculate approximately the normal concentration of the lead and that of the chloride in the solution just before the permanent precipitate first forms, and the corresponding value of the ion-concentration product for lead chloride (assuming the salts are completely ionized). Find the ratio of this product to the saturation-value of it given in Note 6, P. 11. Let the mixture of $Pb(NO_3)_2$ and NH_4Cl stand 3 minutes; note the result, and explain it. Add to the mixture 2 cc. more of the 3 n. NH_4Cl solution, and note and explain the result.

To one drop of the test-solution of $AgNO_3$ in 12 cc. of water in a test-tube add 4 cc. of the 3 n. NH_4Cl solution. Calculate the normal concentration of silver-ion and that of chloride-ion in the solution at the moment of mixing (before the precipitate has separated), assuming that the salts are completely ionized; and find the corresponding value of the ion-concentration product for silver chloride. Calculate also the saturation-value of that product from the solubility of silver chloride given in the Table of Solubilities in the Appendix; and determine also the limit of delicacy of this test for silver by calculating the smallest number of milligrams which, if present in the solution, could have given a precipitate.

Experiment 3. — *Analysis of the Silver-Group.* — Study Table III (preceding P. 11). Mix in a conical flask 20 cc. of the test-solution of $Pb(NO_3)_2$ with 5 cc. portions of the test-solutions of $AgNO_3$ and $Hg_2(NO_3)_2$, and treat the mixture by P. 11–13. Read the Notes on P. 12–13.

* Treat the black residue left by NH_4OH by P. 14. Read the Notes on P. 14.

> * *Note.* — Experiments or parts of experiments preceded by an asterisk may be omitted in brief courses on the subject when the instructor so directs.

Experiment 4. — *Precipitation by Hydrogen Sulfide.* — To 10 cc. of the test-solution of $Bi(NO_3)_3$ add 5 cc. of HNO_3, 4 cc. of 3 n. NH_4Cl solution, and 80 cc. of water; and treat the mixture as described in the second and third sentences of P. 21. Read Notes 3–5 of P. 21.

> *Note.* — The HNO_3 and NH_4Cl are added and the mixture is diluted to 100 cc., so as to have the conditions the same as those prevailing in actual analyses.

Experiment 5. — *Effect of Acid on the Precipitation by Hydrogen Sulfide.* — Introduce into each of three test-tubes by means of a dropper 3 drops of the test-solution of $Cd(NO_3)_2$. Add to the first tube 1 cc. of HCl, to the second 3 cc. of HCl, and to the third 9 cc. of HCl. Then add to each solution enough water to make the volume about 20 cc., and pass a slow current of H_2S into it for about a minute. Repeat the last test (with 9 cc. of HCl), substituting $Cu(NO_3)_2$ for the $Cd(NO_3)_2$. Calculate the normal concentration of the HCl in each tube, and record and explain the results. Study Note 6, P. 21.

* **Experiment 6.** — *Precipitation of Arsenic by Hydrogen Sulfide.* — To 10 cc. of the test-solution of H_3AsO_4 add 5 cc. of HNO_3, 4 cc. of 3 n. NH_4Cl solution, and 80 cc. of water. Treat this mixture by the whole of P. 21, omitting the final filtration. Read Notes 7 and 8, P. 21.

Experiment 7. — *Effect of Oxidizing Substances on Hydrogen Sulfide.* — To 20 cc. of the test-solution of $Fe(NO_3)_3$ add 4 cc. of 3 n. NH_4Cl solution, 5 cc. of HNO_3, and 70 cc. of water, and pass in H_2S till the solution is saturated. Repeat this experiment, substituting 20 cc. of the test-solution of K_2CrO_4 (not the K_2CrO_4 reagent) for that of the $Fe(NO_3)_3$. Study Notes 9 and 10, P. 21.

Experiment 8. — *Analysis of the Copper-Group.* — Study Table V (preceding P. 31). Mix 10 cc. portions of the test-solutions of $Pb(NO_3)_2$, $Bi(NO_3)_3$, $Cu(NO_3)_2$, and $Cd(NO_3)_2$, add 5 cc. of HNO_3, 4 cc. of 3 n. NH_4Cl solution, and 50 cc. of water, treat the mixture by the first paragraph of P. 21, and treat the precipitate so obtained by P. 31–37. Read the Notes on P. 31–37.

Experiment 9. — *Analysis of an Unknown Solution for the Copper-Group.* — Ask the instructor for an unknown solution (Unknown A) containing elements of the copper-group, and analyze 10 cc. of it for those elements. First add 5 cc. of HNO_3 and 4 cc. of 3 n. NH_4Cl solution, and treat the mixture by the first paragraph of P. 21. Treat the precipitate thus obtained by P. 31–37. Estimate the quantities present, and record and report the results, as described in the following directions.

Directions for Analyzing Unknown Solutions. — Estimate the number of milligrams of any constituent present from the size of the precipitate obtained in the Confirmatory Test or in the Procedure preceding it. In order to make this estimate more accurate, compare it, unless the precipitate is obviously very large, with that obtained by subjecting a known quantity of the test-solution directly to the same final Procedure. For this purpose use of the test-solution 0.5 cc. (measured with a dropper) in case the precipitate is small, or 5 cc. (measured in a 10 cc. graduate) in case it is fairly large, or both volumes in separate tests in case it is intermediate in size. (Note that fifteen medium-sized drops correspond to 0.5 cc., and that 0.5 cc. of the test-solution contains 5 mg. of the constituent to be tested for.) Record the analyses of unknown solutions in the note-book in three columns headed Operations, Observations, Conclusions. Enter the operations and observations in the same brief form employed in the experiments with known solutions. In the column headed Conclusions insert the conclusions that may be drawn from each observation as to the presence or absence of any of the constituents that may be present in the unknown solution; and give the estimate made of the number of milligrams present in 10 cc. of the solution. The chemical equations involved need not be written.

After the record has been written up completely in the notebook, report in duplicate the results of the analysis to the instructor in the form shown in the Note below, stating not only the nature of the constituents, but also the approximate quantities of them found present in the 10 cc. of solution. Quantities less than 5 mg. may be reported as " small " (s); those from 5 to 50 mg. as " medium " (m); and those greater than 50 mg. as " large " (l). (It is to be noted, since one gram of a non-metallic solid substance is ordinarily taken for analysis, that 5 mg. corresponds to the presence of 0.5% and 50 mg. to the presence of 5% of the constituent in such a substance.) The instructor will return one of the duplicate reports with an entry on it showing the quantities of the various constituents which the unknown solution actually contained.

The correctness of the results obtained in the analysis of these unknown solutions is an important factor in determining the grade of the student. As the unknowns will contain as little as 2 or 3 mg. of some constituents, satisfactory results can be secured only by careful manipulation and intelligent following of directions.

Note. — Cards with the following heading are conveniently employed for the reports of these analyses of unknown solutions, and of the later analyses of unknown solid substances; space being available below the heading for eight or ten constituents on each half of the card.

NAME.................DATE...........
UNKNOWN NO..........GRADE......

CONSTIT- UENT	QUANT. FOUND	QUANT. PRESENT	CONSTIT- UENT	QUANT. FOUND	QUANT. PRESENT

Experiment 10. — *Behavior of Tin-Group Elements toward Hydrogen Sulfide and Sodium Sulfide.* — Study Table IV (preceding P. 21). To 5 cc. of water in each of four test-tubes add

from a dropper 6 drops of the test-solutions of $HgCl_2$, of $AsCl_3$, of $SbCl_3$, and of H_2SnCl_6, respectively. Pass H_2S into each tube for half a minute. Then add from a graduate 2 cc. of Na_2S reagent. Finally, add 3 cc. of HCl slowly to each tube, and shake the mixture. Compare these precipitates with that produced by mixing 5 cc. of water, 2 cc. of Na_2S reagent, and 3 cc. of HCl, and shaking. Read Notes 2 and 3, P. 22, and Notes 3–5, P. 23.

> *Note.* — In an actual analysis the analyst decides, whenever possible, from the appearance of the HCl precipitate whether or not the tin-group is present in significant quantity. Note that the six drops of the test-solutions used in this experiment correspond to 2 mg. of the constituent.

Experiment 11. — *Separation of the Tin-Group from the Copper-Group.* — Refer to Table IV. To a mixture of 5 cc. portions of the test-solutions of $Bi(NO_3)_3$, $HgCl_2$, $AsCl_3$, $SbCl_3$, and H_2SnCl_6 add 5 cc. of HNO_3, 4 cc. of 3 n. NH_4Cl solution, and enough water to make the volume 100 cc. Treat the mixture by the first paragraph of P. 21, filter with the aid of suction (see Note 2, P. 23), and treat the precipitate by P. 22, using 10 cc. of Na_2S reagent. Reject the residue of Bi_2S_3, and treat the sulfide solution by P. 23. Treat at once the HCl precipitate obtained in P. 23 as described in Expt. 12. Read Notes 4–6, P. 22, and Notes 6–7, P. 23.

Experiment 12. — *Analysis of the Tin-Group.* — Study Table VI (preceding P. 41). Treat the HCl precipitate of the tin-group sulfides obtained in Expt. 11 by P. 41–47. Read the Notes on P. 41–47.

Experiment 13. — *Analysis of Unknown Solutions for the Copper- and Tin-Groups.* — Ask for an unknown solution (Unknown B) containing elements of the tin-group, and another unknown solution (Unknown C) containing elements of the copper-group and tin-group, and analyze 10 cc. of each of them. First, in order to secure the proper acid concentration for the H_2S precipitation, make the solution exactly neutral by adding to it NH_4OH, drop by drop, till it no longer reddens blue litmus paper, and add just 5 cc. of HNO_3 and enough water to make the volume 100 cc. Then treat the mixture by P. 21–23, followed by P. 41–47 in the case of Unknown B, and by P. 31–37 and P. 41–47 in the case of Unknown C.

Experiment 14. — *Detection of Phosphate.* — Pour 1 cc. of the test-solution of $Ca_3(PO_4)_2$ in HNO_3 into a mixture of 2 cc. of HNO_3 and 2 cc. of $(NH_4)_2MoO_4$ reagent, and heat the mixture to 60–70°. Read P. 50 and the Notes on it.

Experiment 15. — *Precipitation of the Aluminum- and Iron-Groups and Solution of the Group-Precipitate.* — Treat a mixture of 10 cc. portions of the test-solutions of $Co(NO_3)_2$ and of $Fe(NO_3)_3$ by P. 51 and by the first paragraph of P. 52, omitting the filtration and evaporation at the end. Refer to Table VII (preceding P. 51), and read Note 1, P. 51, and Notes 1–2, P. 52.

Experiment 16. — *Behavior of Elements of the Aluminum- and Iron-Groups toward Ammonium Hydroxide and Sulfide.* — To 5 cc. portions of the test-solutions of $Al(NO_3)_3$, $Cr(NO_3)_3$, $Fe(NO_3)_3$, $FeCl_2$, $Zn(NO_3)_2$, $Mn(NO_3)_2$, $Ni(NO_3)_2$, and $Co(NO_3)_2$, in separate test-tubes add 1 cc. of 3 n. NH_4Cl solution and 8–10 drops of NH_4OH, and note the result. Then add 2–3 cc. more of NH_4OH. Finally, add 1–2 cc. of 6 n. $(NH_4)_2S$ solution to each tube. Filter out the NiS precipitate, and boil the filtrate for 2 or 3 minutes. Record the results of all these tests in a single table, so as to show what effect is observed and what compound is formed in the case of each element upon the addition of each reagent. Study the results, refer to Table VII, and read Notes 2–5 and 8–10, P. 51.

Experiment 17. — *Behavior of Elements of the Aluminum- and Iron-Groups toward Sodium Hydroxide and Peroxide.* — To separate 5 cc. portions of the test-solutions named in Expt. 16 add 8–10 drops of 6 n. NaOH solution, and note the result. Then add 2–3 cc. more, and again note the result. Finally, to each of the mixtures add gradually from a dry graduate (without using paper) 0.2–0.3 cc. of Na_2O_2 powder, and heat it to boiling. Record all the results in a single table as in Expt. 16. Study the results, refer to Table VII, and read Notes 3–7, P. 52.

Experiment 18. — *Analysis of the Aluminum-Group.* — Study Table VIII (preceding P. 53). Treat a mixture of 10 cc. portions of the test-solutions of $Al(NO_3)_3$, $Zn(NO_3)_2$, and $Cr(NO_3)_3$ by the second paragraph of P. 52 and by P. 53–57. Read the Notes on P. 53–57.

Experiment 19. — *Analysis of the Iron-Group : Separation of Manganese and Iron.* — Study Table IX (preceding P. 61), considering only the case where " phosphate is absent." Treat a mixture of 10 cc. portions of the test-solutions of $Mn(NO_3)_2$, $Fe(NO_3)_3$, $Co(NO_3)_2$, and $Ni(NO_3)_2$ and of a 2 cc. portion of that of $Zn(NO_3)_2$ by the second paragraph of P. 52; and treat the precipitate thereby obtained by P. 61, 62, and 63. Treat the filtrate containing the zinc, cobalt, and nickel as described in Expt. 20. Read the Notes on P. 61, 62, and 63.

*Experiment 20. — *Analysis of the Iron-Group : Separation of Zinc, Cobalt, and Nickel.* — Study Table X (preceding P. 66). Treat the filtrate obtained in Expt. 19 by P. 65–68. Read the Notes on P. 65–68.

> *Note.* — In brief courses this experiment may be omitted. And in the unknowns subsequently given for analysis nickel (but not cobalt) may be included, it being detected by passing H_2S into the filtrate from the NH_4OH precipitate (P. 63) as described in the first sentence of P. 65; and zinc need be tested for only in the analysis of the aluminum-group.

Experiment 21. — *Analysis of an Unknown Solution for Elements of the Aluminum- and Iron-Groups.* — Ask the instructor for an unknown solution for this purpose (Unknown D), and treat 10 cc. of it by P. 51–57, 61–63, and 65–68, first diluting it with 90 cc. of water.

*Experiment 22. — *Precipitation of Alkaline-Earth Elements by Ammonium Hydroxide in the Presence of Phosphate.* — Heat 0.2 cc. of $Ca_3(PO_4)_2$ powder with 10 cc. of water; then add 5 cc. of HNO_3, and boil the mixture for one minute. To the solution add NH_4OH till the mixture, after shaking, smells of it; filter, and add 1 cc. of $(NH_4)_2CO_3$ reagent to the filtrate. Repeat the experiment, using 0.2 cc. of $CaCO_3$ powder in place of the $Ca_3(PO_4)_2$. Explain in the note-book why the calcium is precipitated by NH_4OH in one case and not in the other. Read Notes 6–7, P. 51, and Note 8, P. 52.

*Experiment 23. — *Modification of the Analysis of the Iron-Group in the Presence of Phosphate for the Purpose of Detecting Alkaline-Earth Elements.* — Mix together 10 cc. portions of the test-solutions of $Fe(NO_3)_3$ and of $Co(NO_3)_2$, and of that of $Ca_3(PO_4)_2$ in HNO_3. Treat this solution by the last paragraph of P. 64 and by P. 65. To the filtrate obtained in P. 65 add 2–3 cc. of $(NH_4)_2CO_3$ reagent. Read the Notes on P. 64.

*Experiment 24. — *Analysis of an Unknown Solution for Elements of the Aluminum- and Iron-Groups in the Presence of Phosphate.* — Ask the instructor for an unknown solution for this purpose (Unknown E), and treat 10 cc. of it by P. 51–57 and 61–68.

Experiment 25. — *Precipitation of the Alkaline-Earth Group.* — To 2 cc. of the test-solution of $Mg(NO_3)_2$ add 8 cc. of water and 2 cc. of $(NH_4)_2CO_3$ reagent, and shake the mixture for about a minute; then add 5 cc. of $(NH_4)_2CO_3$ reagent and 5 cc. of 95% ethyl alcohol, and shake for a minute more. Repeat the experiment, using the test-solution of $Ca(NO_3)_2$ in place of that of $Mg(NO_3)_2$, and filtering out any precipitate before adding the second portion of $(NH_4)_2CO_3$ reagent. Read P. 71 and the Notes on it.

Experiment 26. — *Analysis of the Alkaline-Earth Group.* — Study Table XI (preceding P. 71). Mix in a 100 cc. flask 3 cc. portions of the test-solutions of $BaCl_2$, $Sr(NO_3)_2$, $Ca(NO_3)_2$, and $Mg(NO_3)_2$; and treat the solution by the second paragraph of P. 71, followed by P. 72–79. Read the Notes on P. 72–79.

Experiment 27. — *Analysis of the Alkali-Group by the Shorter Less Exact Method.* — Read the General Discussion and study Table XII (preceding P. 81). Mix 10 cc. of the test-solution of KNO_3 and 10 cc. of that of $NaNO_3$ with 4 cc. of 3 n. NH_4Cl solution and 5 cc. of $(NH_4)_2CO_3$ reagent, and treat the mixture by P. 81–83. Read the Notes on P. 81–83.

* **Experiment 28.** — *Analysis of the Alkali-Group by the Exact Method.* — Study Table XIII (preceding P. 85). Prepare the same mixture as in Expt. 27, add to it 1 cc. of the test-solution of Na_2SO_4, and treat it by P. 85–89. Read the Notes on P. 85–89.

Experiment 29. — *Analysis of an Unknown Solution for Elements of the Alkaline-Earth and Alkali-Groups.* — Ask the instructor for an unknown solution for this purpose (Unknown F), and analyze 10 cc. of it by P. 71–79 and P. 81–83,*or by P. 71–79 and P. 85–89.

* **Experiment 30.** — *Detection of Ammonium.* — Treat 0.2 g. of NH_4Cl by P. 91. Read the Notes on P. 91.

* **Experiment 31.** — *Determination of the State of Oxidation of Certain Elements Existing in Two Such States.* —Read the General Discussion and study Table XIV (preceding P. 91). Treat 0.2 g. of finely powdered Fe_3O_4 (ferro-ferric oxide) as described in the first two paragraphs of P. 92. Read the Notes on P. 92.

Experiment 32. — *Analysis of Unknown Solutions for All the Basic Constituents.* — Ask the instructor for two unknown solutions for this purpose (Unknowns G and H), and analyze 10 cc. of each of them by P. 11–92. Before precipitating with H_2S, exactly neutralize the solution with NH_4OH and add 5 cc. of HCl.

DETECTION OF ACIDIC CONSTITUENTS IN NON-IGNEOUS PRODUCTS

Experiment 33. — *Preparation of a Solution for Detecting the Acidic Constituents.* — Read the General Discussion of the Detection of Acidic Constituents (preceding P. 100). Treat 1 g. of the solid test-mixture consisting of 30% of BiOCl, 30% of $Fe_2(SO_4)_3$, 30% of $NaNO_3$, and 10% of Na_2SO_3 by the first paragraph of P. 101, but using only 10 cc. of the Na_2CO_3 solution and diluting the filtrate to only 12 cc. Reserve the filtrate for use in Expts. 34, 36, and 37. Read the Notes on P. 101.

Experiment 34. — *Detection of the Chloride-Group.* — Study the first column of Table XV (preceding P. 102). Treat a portion of the Na_2CO_3 solution prepared in Expt. 33 by P. 102. Read Note 1, P. 102.

Experiment 35. — *Behavior of Acidic Constituents toward Silver Nitrate.* — To separate 2 cc. portions of the test-solutions of Na_2S, NaCN, KI, KBr, NaCl, KSCN, $NaNO_2$, Na_2HPO_4, and K_2CrO_4, add a few drops of $AgNO_3$ solution, and then 1 cc. of HNO_3. Read Notes 2–4, P. 102.

Experiment 36. — *Detection of the Sulfate-Group.* — Study the second column of Table XV. Treat a portion of the Na_2CO_3 solution prepared in Expt. 33 by P. 103. Read the Notes on P. 103.

Experiment 37. — *Detection of Oxidizing and Reducing Constituents.* — Study the last two columns of Table XV. Treat separate portions of the Na_2CO_3 solution prepared in Expt. 33 by P. 104 and 105. Read the Notes on these Procedures.

Experiment 38. — *Identification of Constituents by the Group-Reagents.* — Ask the instructor for two unknown solutions (Unknowns I and J), each of which will contain only one acidic constituent. Add to 5 cc. of each of these solutions 5 cc. of 3 n. Na_2CO_3 solution, and treat portions of the mixture by P. 102–105. On the basis of the results of these tests, taking into account the colors of the precipitates, report what possibilities exist as to the nature of the single constituent present in each solution.

Experiment 39. — *Analysis of the Chloride-Group.* — Study Table XVI (preceding P. 106). Mix 2 cc. portions of the test-solutions of Na_2S, $NaCN$, $K_4Fe(CN)_6$, KI, KBr, $NaCl$, $KSCN$, and $NaClO_3$. Add to the mixture 5 cc. of 3 n. Na_2CO_3 solution, and treat it by P. 106, 107, and the first paragraph of P. 108; reserving the $Ni(NO_3)_2$ and $AgNO_3$ precipitates for use in Expts. 40 and 41. Read the Notes on P. 106 and 107, and Notes 1–2, P. 108.

*Experiment 40. — *Detection of the Different Cyanides.* — Study Table XVII (preceding P. 109). Treat the $Ni(NO_3)_2$ precipitate obtained in Expt. 39 by the first three paragraphs of P. 109. Read the Notes on P. 109.

Experiment 41. — *Detection of Thiocyanate and the Different Halides.* — Study Table XVIII (preceding P. 110). Treat the $AgNO_3$ precipitate obtained in Expt. 39 by P. 110. Read the Notes on P. 110.

*Experiment 42. — *Detection of Hypochlorite and of Chlorate.* — Treat 0.5 g. of bleaching powder by the second paragraph of P. 108. Read Notes 3 and 4, P. 108.

Experiment 43. — *Analysis of an Unknown Solution for Constituents of the Chloride-Group.* — Ask the instructor for an unknown solution (Unknown K) for this purpose. To 5 cc. of it add 1 cc. of 3 n. Na_2CO_3 solution. Treat the mixture by P. 106, 107, and the first paragraph of P. 108. Treat the $AgNO_3$ precipitate by P. 110. *Treat the $Ni(NO_3)_2$ precipitate by P. 109.

Experiment 44. — *Analysis of the Sulfate-Group.* — Study Table XIX (preceding P. 111). Mix 2 cc. portions of the test-solutions of Na_2S, Na_2SO_4, Na_2SO_3, and NaF. Add to the mixture 5 cc. of 3 n. Na_2CO_3 solution, and treat it by P. 111–112. Read the Notes on P. 111–112.

Experiment 45. — *Detection of Nitrate or Nitrite.* — Study the first two columns of Table XX (preceding P. 113). Add 1 cc. of the test-solution of $NaNO_2$ to 2 cc. of 3 n. Na_2CO_3 solution, and treat the mixture by P. 113. Read the Notes on P. 113.

Experiment 46. — *Detection of Nitrite.* — Add 3 drops of the test-solution of $NaNO_2$ to 1 cc. of 3 n. Na_2CO_3 solution, and treat the mixture by P. 114. Read the Notes on P. 114.

Experiment 47. — *Detection of Borate.* — Refer to the third column of Table XX. Evaporate to dryness in small casseroles a 5-drop portion and a 2-cc. portion of the test-solution of $NaBO_2$; and to each of the residues add 3 cc. of 3 n. Na_2CO_3 solution. Treat these mixtures, and also 3 cc. of 3 n. Na_2CO_3 solution to which no $NaBO_2$ is added, by P. 115. Read the Notes on P. 115.

*Experiment 48. — *Detection of Arsenate and Arsenite.* — Study the last column of Table XX. Treat by P. 116 a mixture of 2 cc. of the test-solution of H_3AsO_4, 2 cc. of the test-solution of $NaAsO_2$, and 4 cc. of 3 n. Na_2CO_3 solution. Read the Notes on P. 116.

Experiment 49. — *Analysis of an Unknown Solution for the Acidic Constituents Tested for in Sodium Carbonate Solution.* — Ask the instructor for an unknown solution (Unknown L) for this purpose. To 10 cc. of it add 20 cc. of 3 n. Na_2CO_3 solution, and treat portions of the mixture by P. 102–116.

DETECTION OF ACIDIC CONSTITUENTS IN NATURAL SUBSTANCES
AND IGNEOUS PRODUCTS

Experiment 50. — *Detection of Sulfate, Carbonate, Sulfide, and Cyanide.* — Study Table XXI (preceding P. 121). Treat 0.5 g. of the test-mixture consisting of 60% of gypsum ($CaSO_4 \cdot 2 H_2O$), 20% of marble ($CaCO_3$), 10% of pyrite (FeS_2), and 10% of KCN, as directed in the first, second, and fourth paragraphs of P. 121. Read the Notes on P. 117 and 121.

Experiment 51. — *Detection of Chloride, Fluoride, and Borate.* — Study Table XXII (preceding P. 122). Treat 1 g. of the test-mixture consisting of 5% of salt (NaCl), 5% of fluorite (CaF_2), 5% of borax ($Na_2B_4O_7$), and 85% of fine sand by P. 122, omitting the confirmatory test for fluoride and the comparison of the borate color with standards. Read the Notes on P. 122.

PREPARATION OF THE SOLUTION FOR THE DETECTION OF BASIC
CONSTITUENTS AND THE COMPLETE ANALYSIS OF
UNKNOWN SUBSTANCES

Experiment 52. — *Indications of Certain Constituents Afforded
by the Closed-Tube Test.* — Treat separately by the first paragraph of P. 1 samples of the following substances: $NaC_2H_3O_2$,
$Cu(NO_3)_2 \cdot 3H_2O$, NH_4Cl, and FeS_2. Read the Notes on P. 1,
and write the equations expressing the reactions involved (except
in the case of the $NaC_2H_3O_2$).

General Directions for Complete Analyses. — Record the
results in the note-book and report them in the way explained
in the Directions for Analyzing Unknown Solutions (preceding
Expt. 10). In the case of solid substances, not only report the
constituents found present and the quantities of them estimated
to be contained in one gram of the substance, but state also the
compound or compounds of which the substance seems to be
mainly composed. Submit the reports to the instructor in
duplicate on cards like those described in the Directions for
Analyzing Unknown Solutions.

The quantity of a solid substance taken for the analysis should
be weighed (within 0.1 g.) on a rough balance, not guessed at
nor estimated by volume.

In analyses where a number of different precipitates and
filtrates are successively obtained, any of these that are set
aside, even temporarily, should be distinctly labeled, in order
to avoid mistakes. A convenient method of doing this is to
mark on the label simply the Procedure by which the precipitate
or filtrate is next to be treated; thus the H_2S precipitate would
be marked P. 22, and the filtrate from it P. 51. The final tests
for any element may be marked Test for Pb, Test for Al, etc.

Experiment 53. — *Analysis of Non-Metallic Substances Dissolved by Water or Dilute Acid.* — Ask the instructor for two
such non-igneous substances (Unknowns 1 and 2), and treat
samples of each of them as directed in P. 1. Read the Notes on
P. 2; and study the General Statement relating to Solubilities in
the Appendix.

c

Experiment 54. — *Analysis of Non-Metallic Substances Dis-solved only by Concentrated Acids.* — Study the upper part of Table I (preceding P. 2). Ask the instructor for two non-igneous products and two natural substances or igneous products dissolved only by concentrated acids (Unknowns 3, 4, 5, and 6), and treat samples of each of them as directed in P. 1. If there is any residue undissolved at the end of P. 3, disregard it in these practice analyses. Read the Notes on P. 3.

Experiment 55. — *Analysis of Alloys.* — Ask the instructor for two alloys (Unknowns 7 and 8), and treat a sample of each as directed in P. 4, followed by P. 21–78. Read the Notes on P. 4.

*** Experiment 56.** — *Analysis of Natural Substances or Igneous Products Not Completely Dissolved by Treatment with Nitric and Hydrochloric Acids.* — Study the lower part of Table I (preceding P. 2). Ask the instructor for two such substances (Unknowns 9 and 10). Treat 1 g. of each of them by P. 2, 3, 5, and 6, followed by P. 11–89. Treat fresh samples of each of the substances by P. 121 and 122. Read the Notes on P. 5 and 6.

Ask the instructor for another such substance (Unknown 11). Treat 1 g. of it by P. 2 and 3. Treat the solution obtained in P. 3 by P. 21–89, and the residue undissolved in P. 3 as directed in P. 7. Treat fresh samples of the substance by P. 121 and 122. Read the Notes on P. 7 and 123.

*** Experiment 57.** — *Analysis of Non-Igneous Products Con-taining Organic Matter.* — Ask the instructor for such a substance (Unknown 12), and treat a sample of it by P. 1, another sample as directed in P. 8, and a third sample as directed in P. 100. Read the Notes on P. 8.

*** Experiment 58.** — *Analysis of Solutions.* — Ask the instructor for an aqueous solution which is a trade preparation (Unknown 13), and treat it as described in P. 9. Read the Notes on P. 9.

QUESTIONS ON THE EXPERIMENTS

DETECTION OF THE BASIC CONSTITUENTS

Experiment 1. — *Separation of the Basic Constituents into Groups.* —
1. In precipitating the silver-group in an actual analysis could the NH_4Cl be replaced by $NaCl$? by HCl? Why or why not?

2. If the NH_4Cl were not added, what would happen to the silver in the subsequent parts of the experiment?

3. Of the five basic constituents present in the mixture why is silver the only one that is precipitated by NH_4Cl?

4. If enough H_2S were not used to precipitate all the copper, how would it behave on the subsequent addition of NH_4OH and $(NH_4)_2S$?

5. What is the first reaction that takes place when NH_4OH is added to the filtrate from the H_2S precipitate?

6. What would happen to the $(NH_4)_2S$ if it were added directly to the filtrate from the H_2S precipitate, without first adding NH_4OH?

7. What happens to the $(NH_4)_2S$ when the filtrate from the $(NH_4)_2S$ precipitate is evaporated?

8. If all the basic constituents had been present in the original mixture used for this experiment, what ones would have been precipitated by (*a*) NH_4Cl, (*b*) H_2S, (*c*) NH_4OH and $(NH_4)_2S$, (*d*) $(NH_4)_2CO_3$? (*e*) What ones would have been left with the potassium in the filtrate from the $(NH_4)_2CO_3$ precipitate?

Experiment 2. — *Precipitation of the Silver-Group. Principles Relating to Equivalents, Concentration, and Solubility-Effect.* — 1. What would be meant by the statement that a certain quantity of lead nitrate is equivalent to a certain other quantity of ammonium chloride?

2. In making up one liter of 3 n. NH_4Cl, how many grams of the salt should be weighed out, and how much water should be added to it? (For the atomic-weight values needed in answering this and other questions see the table in the Appendix.)

3. In making up a liter of 6 n. H_2SO_4, how many cubic centimeters of 95% sulfuric acid (s. g., 1.84) should be used, and how much water should be added to it?

4. Approximately how many cubic centimeters of 3 n. NH_4Cl solution would be required to precipitate 500 mg. of silver? (Calculate first the number of equivalents corresponding to 500 mg. Ag.) (Since 1 g. of the unknown substance is ordinarily taken for the analysis for basic constituents, 500 mg. is as large a quantity of any element as is likely to be present.)

5. In general, how many cubic centimeters of a 1 n. reagent must be added to react with 500 mg. of an element which has an equivalent weight of 100? of 50? of 20? (This principle should be frequently applied throughout the System of Analysis; with its aid the number of cubic centimeters of any reagent theoretically required to precipitate the maximum amount of an element likely to be present can quickly be estimated.)

6. Estimate the volume of 3 n. Na_2CO_3 solution required to precipitate 500 mg. of calcium. Estimate the volume of 6 n. NH_4OH required to precipitate 500 mg. of iron when present in the form of $Fe(NO_3)_3$.

7. Explain by the solubility-product principle why $PbCl_2$ is less soluble in a solution containing NH_4Cl than in pure water. (This question may be answered by shortening the complete explanation given in Note 6, P. 11, as follows: " In any dilute sol'n satur. with $PbCl_2$, $(Pb^{++}) \times (Cl^-)^2 =$ satur. value. NH_4Cl added to such a sol'n causes, owing to its ionization into NH_4^+ and Cl^-, an increase in (Cl^-), and therefore raises $(Pb^{++}) \times (Cl^-)^2$ above the saturation value, so that $PbCl_2$ ppts." (*All other questions as to the effect of one substance on the solubility of another substance should be answered in a similar way. Always consider the effect which the added substance may have on the concentration of each of the ions of the salt with which the solution is saturated, and state the reason for any such effect.*)

8. Calculate by the solubility-product principle, from the fact that the solubility of $PbCl_2$ in water at 20° is 0.070 normal, what its solubility would be in a solution 0.40 normal in chloride-ion (which is approximately the chloride-ion concentration in the 0.63 normal NH_4Cl solution). Assume the $PbCl_2$ to be completely ionized.

9. From the result found in Question 8 calculate how many milligrams of lead would have to be present in 15 cc. of water at 20°, in order that precipitation of $PbCl_2$ may result on adding to it 4 cc. of 3 n. NH_4Cl solution. (Owing to the tendency to form supersaturated solutions, a much larger quantity of lead may actually be present before precipitation occurs.)

10. Compute the number of milligrams of mercurous mercury that must be present in 15 cc. of water in order that it could precipitate on the addition of 4 cc. of 3 n. NH_4Cl solution, taking into account the facts that Hg_2Cl_2 has a solubility of 0.000002 normal and that its molecule dissociates into one Hg_2^{++} ion and two Cl^- ions.

Experiment 3. — *Analysis of the Silver-Group* — 1. Why is a considerable excess of NH_4Cl added in precipitating the silver-group? (The term *excess* signifies the quantity added beyond the equivalent quantity theoretically required to produce the reaction in question.)

2. Explain why, in apparent contravention of the solubility-product principle, a large excess of NH_4Cl would increase the solubility of the silver-group chlorides. (This difference in the solubility-effect of a slight excess

and of a large excess of a reagent is a phenomenon frequently met with in analytical chemistry, and it commonly arises from the same kind of influence as is here involved.)

3. What might happen if the solution of the nitrates to which the NH_4Cl solution is added had a much larger volume than 15 cc.?

4. Why is the precipitate of the silver-group chlorides washed with dilute HCl rather than with water? Could it be washed with dilute NH_4Cl solution equally well?

5. The solubility of AgCl at 100° is 0.022 g. per liter. How many milligrams of silver might be lost if 100 cc. of boiling water were used for extracting the lead from the chloride precipitate?

6. With what other reagents besides K_2CrO_4 might the hot-water extract be tested for lead? (See the Table of Solubilities in the Appendix.) What advantage does K_2CrO_4 have over each of these other reagents with respect to the delicacy or to the characteristicness of the test?

7. Explain by the solubility-product principle why the formation of the complex salt $Ag(NH_3)_2{}^+Cl^-$ causes AgCl to be much more soluble in NH_4OH solution than in water. (Answer in accordance with the Note on Question 7, Expt. 2.)

8. Formulate the mass-action expression for the equilibrium between the complex cation $Ag(NH_3)_2{}^+$ and its constituents. Show by reference to this expression and the solubility-product principle why the addition of HNO_3 causes AgCl to be precipitated out of its solution in NH_4OH.

Experiments 4 and 5. — *Precipitation by Hydrogen Sulfide.* — 1. In the precipitation of bismuth caused by diluting the solution with water, what ion-concentration product comes into consideration? What must be true of its value in order that bismuth may be precipitated? Explain why decreasing the HNO_3 concentration decreases the quantity of bismuth that remains in solution.

2. In precipitating with H_2S what is the reason for adding 5 cc. of HNO_3 and diluting the solution to 100 cc.? Why not use less acid and thus avoid all risk of failing to precipitate the elements of the copper- and tin-groups?

3. In passing H_2S into a $Cu(NO_3)_2$ solution, at what stage in the process does the solution after shaking begin to smell of the gas?

4. Write the chemical equation expressing the precipitation of copper-ion by dissolved H_2S. By formulating the corresponding mass-action expression, show how the concentration of copper-ion remaining unprecipitated is related to the H_2S concentration and the H^+ ion concentration. (Note that the same would be true of any bivalent metal ion.)

5. What principle determines how the concentration of H_2S, that is, the quantity of it dissolved by a unit-volume of water, varies with its partial pressure? What would its partial pressure be in a mixture made by mixing 1 volume of H_2S with 4 volumes of air at a pressure of 1 atmosphere?

6. Why would a larger quantity of an element have to be present in order to give a precipitate if the solution were treated with H_2S in an open beaker, instead of in the closed flask?

7. Give two reasons why a larger quantity of an element would have to be present to give a precipitate if the solution were saturated with H_2S at 80°, instead of at 20°.

8. The solubility (in equivalents per liter) of freshly precipitated ZnS in water is about 1000 times as great as that of CdS. Calculate by the principles discussed in Note 6, P. 21, the ratio of the hydrogen-ion concentrations at which the precipitation of cadmium and zinc will barely take place when the concentration of each of them has any definite value (for example, 0.0001 equivalents per liter).

9. The pressure-volume relations of perfect gases are expressed by the equation $pv/T = 82\ N$, when the pressure p is in atmospheres, the volume v in cubic centimeters, and the temperature T in centigrade-degrees on the absolute scale, and when the quantity of the gas is N gram-molecular-weights. Calculate the number of cubic centimeters of H_2S at 25° required to precipitate 500 mg. of copper.

Experiment 6. — *Precipitation of Arsenic by Hydrogen Sulfide.* — 1. By what reaction is the HNO_3 destroyed when the arsenic solution to which HCl has been added is evaporated to dryness? Could HCl be destroyed in the same way by evaporating a solution of chloride with HNO_3?

2. If the HNO_3 were not so destroyed, what would happen when the H_2S is passed into the hot, strongly acid solution?

3. What difference in ionization relations accounts for the facts that, unlike the other elements, arsenic in the form of H_3AsO_4 is only very slowly precipitated from a cold, weakly acid solution, and that its precipitation is greatly promoted by increasing the HCl concentration?

4. Write the series of reactions that occur when H_2S is passed into a dilute HCl solution of H_3AsO_4.

Experiment 7. — *Effect of Oxidizing Substances on Hydrogen Sulfide.* — 1. What substances besides ferric salts might be present which would liberate sulfur from H_2S?

2. Write the equation expressing the reaction between each of these substances and H_2S, balancing the equations by the method described in Note 10, P. 21.

3. Write by the same method the equations expressing the oxidation of H_2S, in one case to sulfur and in another to H_2SO_4, by hot, fairly concentrated HNO_3, assuming that the HNO_3 is reduced to NO.

Experiment 8. — *Analysis of the Copper-Group.* — 1. Make a table showing briefly in the first column the chemical operations involved in analyzing a solution for lead and bismuth (by P. 21 and P. 31–35), and showing in a second and in a third column the behavior of these two elements in each operation. " Behavior " in this and later questions means both the effect observed and the chemical compound produced. Thus, the first two operations and the results of them in the case of lead should be entered as follows:

Operation	Behavior of Lead
Saturate with H_2S.	Black ppt. of PbS.
Boil with 3 n. HNO_3.	Ppt. diss., forming colorless sol'n of $Pb^{++}(NO_3^-)_2$.

2. Make a similar table showing the operations involved in analyzing a solution for copper and cadmium (by P. 21, 31, 32, 34, 36, and 37), and showing the behavior of these elements.

3. Explain by the solubility-product principle the fact that CuS, which is only slightly soluble in hot dilute HCl, dissolves readily in hot dilute HNO_3 of the same concentration.

4. Write the equation expressing the dissolving of CuS in 3 n. HNO_3.

5. Why may a black residue be left undissolved by HNO_3?

6. Why does the evaporation with H_2SO_4 convert the salts present into sulfates? Could sulfates be converted into nitrates by evaporating with a large excess of HNO_3?

7. Explain with reference to the solubility-product principle why $PbSO_4$ is much more soluble in dilute HNO_3 than in water. (H_2SO_4 in dilute solution is dissociated almost completely into H^+ and HSO_4^-; but the latter ion is only to a moderate extent dissociated into H^+ and $SO_4^=$.)

8. What effect, as compared with that of HNO_3, would HCl have on the solubility of $PbSO_4$? What effect would KNO_3 have? Give reasons. (K_2SO_4 in dilute solution, like other unibivalent salts, but unlike H_2SO_4, is almost completely dissociated into the simple ions, K^+ and SO_4^-, with formation of only a small proportion of the intermediate ion, KSO_4^-.)

9. Explain by the solubility-product principle why the fact that $PbAc_2$ is a slightly ionized substance should cause $PbSO_4$ to dissolve much more readily in NH_4Ac solution than in water.

10. Would one expect $PbCrO_4$ also to be more soluble in NH_4Ac solution than in water? Why or why not? If so, why does $PbCrO_4$ precipitate from the same NH_4Ac solution that dissolves $PbSO_4$?

11. Explain with the aid of the mass-action expressions involved why $Cu(OH)_2$, a substance very slightly soluble in water, is not precipitated by the NH_4OH. Show that the presence of the $(NH_4)_2SO_4$ in the solution must diminish the tendency of it to precipitate.

12. If the lead were not removed by the addition of H_2SO_4, would it be precipitated as $Pb(OH)_2$ on the addition of an excess of NH_4OH? What

knowledge in regard to lead compounds would enable one to predict whether or not this precipitation would take place?

13. Write the equations expressing the formation of Na_2SnO_2 from $SnCl_2$ and $NaOH$; also that expressing the spontaneous decomposition of Na_2SnO_2 into Sn and Na_2SnO_3; also that expressing its action on BiO_3H_3.

14. Lead hydroxide, like $Sn(OH)_2$, is an amphoteric substance. What is meant by this statement? What experiments might be made to determine whether it is true?

15. The presence of bismuth in the NH_4OH precipitate can be confirmed by dissolving and reprecipitating as $BiOCl$. Describe a procedure by which this confirmatory test could be made so as to be delicate, taking into account the fact that $BiOCl$, though very slightly soluble in water, increases rapidly in solubility as the concentration of acid in the solution increases.

16. If $(NH_4)_2S$ be added to the NH_4OH solution, both CuS and CdS are precipitated. What does this show as to the degree of dissociation of the complex ammonia ions of these elements into the simple ions?

17. If $K_4Fe(CN)_6$ be added to the NH_4OH solution (without neutralizing it with HAc), no precipitate results unless a fairly large quantity of copper is present. Explain this fact.

18. With the aid of the Table of Molal Reduction-Potentials in the Appendix show by computation of the actual reduction-potentials whether copper would be precipitated till its concentration became as small as 0.0001 formal by metallic Pb (as it is by metallic Fe), assuming its ions attained in the process a concentration of 0.1 formal.

19. Show by similar computations whether lead and bismuth (if not previously removed by the H_2SO_4 and NH_4OH) would, like copper, be almost quantitatively precipitated by metallic Fe.

20. CdS, though very slightly soluble in water, is much more soluble in it than is CuS (as illustrated by Expt. 5). Outline a series of experiments that might be made to determine whether on this fact could be based a procedure by which 1 mg. of cadmium could be detected in the presence of 500 mg. of copper.

Experiments 10 and 11. — *Separation of the Tin- and Copper-Groups.* — 1. Write chemical equations expressing the two stages of the hydrolysis of Na_2S. Explain by the ionic theory and the mass-action law why this hydrolysis takes place, taking account of the fact that water is ionized to a slight extent into H^+ and OH^-.

2. A solution made by dissolving crystals of $Na_2S \cdot 9 H_2O$ in water has a strong alkaline reaction to litmus, a pronounced slippery feel, and scarcely any odor. What conclusions may be drawn from these facts as to the degree to which each stage of the hydrolysis has taken place?

3. Explain by the mass-action law how the presence of NaOH in the Na_2S reagent decreases the hydrolysis of the salt.

4. Write equations expressing the action of HCl on the Na_2S and on the Na_2S_2 present in the reagent.

5. What is the main purpose of having a certain proportion of Na_2S_2 in the reagent?

6. Write equations showing the behavior of $SnCl_2$ and of H_2SnCl_6 when treated in succession with H_2S by P. 21, with Na_2S reagent by P. 22, and with HCl by P. 23.

7. Explain by the mass-action law why the addition of HCl to a solution of Na_2SnS_3 causes the precipitation of SnS_2.

8. In what respects is the separation of the elements of the copper-group from those of the tin-group by the Na_2S reagent imperfect?

9. If $(NH_4)_2S$ is used for the separation, mercury remains as HgS almost completely with the elements of the copper-group, instead of passing into the sulfide solution. Suggest an explanation of this striking difference in behavior, taking into account that the only differences in the two solutions are those arising from the fact that NH_4OH is a slightly ionized base and NaOH a largely ionized one.

Experiment 12. — *Analysis of the Tin-Group.* — 1. Describe the differences in the solubilities of the sulfides of mercury, arsenic, antimony, and tin on which the separation of these elements from one another is based.

2. In treating the sulfides with 12 n. HCl why does much more As_2S_5 dissolve if the solution be allowed to boil? Why does the solution boil at so low a temperature as $50-60°$?

3. Write by the method described in Note 10, P. 21, the equations expressing the action of HCl on $KClO_3$ by which Cl_2 is produced and that by which ClO_2 is produced.

4. Suggest a reason why in the confirmatory test for mercury the presence of HCl tends to prevent the immediate reduction of Hg_2Cl_2 to Hg.

5. Explain why the Cl_2 set free by the addition of the $KClO_3$ causes the HgS to dissolve even in the dilute HCl.

6. What is the expression for the solubility-product in the case of $MgNH_4AsO_4$? Why does it dissolve readily in HCl? (See the Table of Ionization-Values in the Appendix.)

7. Why does the hydrolysis of this salt increase its solubility? Why is that hydrolysis decreased by an excess of NH_4OH? How is the hydrolysis affected by the presence of NH_4Cl? Would NH_4Cl affect the solubility in any other way?

8. What is a saturated solution? a supersaturated one? By what treatments can a precipitate be made to separate from a supersaturated solution?

9. With the aid of the Table of Molal Reduction-Potentials in the

Appendix state what metals other than Sn would precipitate Sb from a solution 1 n. in HCl. What is the objection to using a more strongly reducing metal in place of tin?

10. State what might be expected to happen on placing metallic Pb in a solution 0.1 n. in $SnCl_2$ and 1 n. in HCl.

11. Show what metals (if any) other than Sb could be used for reducing tin from the stannic to the stannous state in chloride solution, without precipitating nearly all of the tin as metal.

12. What is the significance of the fact that the specific reduction-potential of tin has a positive value, and that of antimony a negative one? How might this fact be made the basis of a method of separating the two metals if they had been precipitated together?

13. Write chemical equations expressing the formation of NaOBr from Br_2 and NaOH, its spontaneous decomposition into NaBr and $NaBrO_3$, and the action of it on metallic As.

14. How does the confirmatory test for tin with $HgCl_2$ differ in type from the usual method of detecting an element?

15. Explain with reference to the reduction-potentials involved why in 1 n. HCl solution a small proportion of $SnCl_2$ reduces $HgCl_2$ to Hg_2Cl_2, and an excess of $SnCl_2$ reduces it to Hg.

16. Predict from the reduction-potentials involved whether the presence of iron in the antimony used as reagent, and hence of $FeCl_2$ in the solution, would cause reduction of the $HgCl_2$ to Hg_2Cl_2.

17. State how any antimony that remained as Sb_2S_5 in the residue undissolved by the treatment with 12 n. HCl in P. 41 would behave in the subsequent procedures (P. 42 and 44). (In answering questions of this type any needed information not otherwise available can usually be secured by simple test-tube experiments.)

18. State how any mercury and any arsenic that went into solution in the 12 n. HCl in P. 41 would behave in the subsequent procedures (P. 45–47).

19. State how any antimony that failed to be precipitated as Sb_2S_3 in P. 45 would behave in P. 47.

Experiment 14. — *Detection of Phosphate.* — 1. Show by the mass-action law why a large concentration of hydrogen-ion promotes the formation of the complex phosphomolybdate anion, noting that MoO_3 is the anhydride of H_2MoO_4 and that the concentration of the latter must determine that of the former when equilibrium is reached.

2. What might be expected to be the effect of NH_4OH on the yellow precipitate of ammonium phosphomolybdate?

3. Give a plausible reason why heating promotes the precipitation of ammonium phosphomolybdate, even though it is probably more soluble in hot solutions.

Experiment 15. — *Precipitation of the Aluminium- and Iron-Groups.* — 1. In an actual analysis how many cubic centimeters of NH_4OH would be required to neutralize the 5 cc. of HNO_3 that are added before precipitating with H_2S?

2. How much more NH_4OH would be needed to neutralize the solution if 500 mg. Cu had been present in the form of $Cu(NO_3)_2$ in the solution precipitated by H_2S? (In all such calculations of the volume of the reagent needed, first reduce the weight of the constituent from grams to equivalents.)

3. How does testing the vapors above the solution with $PbAc_2$ paper show that an excess of $(NH_4)_2S$, a non-volatile salt, has been added?

4. If in an actual analysis the mixture containing NH_4OH and $(NH_4)_2S$ were allowed to absorb CO_2 from the air before filtering, what difference would it make?

5. Why is the $(NH_4)_2S$ precipitate treated first with cold HCl? Why is $KClO_3$ subsequently added?

Experiments 16 and 17. — *Behavior toward Ammonium and Sodium Hydroxides.* — 1. Which elements are soluble: (*a*) in excess of NH_4OH (in the presence of NH_4Cl), but not in excess of NaOH; (*b*) in excess of NaOH, but not of NH_4OH (in presence of NH_4Cl); (*c*) in excess both of NH_4OH and of NaOH; (*d*) neither in excess of NaOH nor of NH_4OH (in presence of NH_4Cl)?

2. What are the explanations of the four typical cases (*a*), (*b*), (*c*), (*d*), referred to in the preceding question?

3. Could the hydroxide of an element which does not form a complex ammonia cation be soluble in NH_4OH and not in NaOH? Could a hydroxide be readily soluble in NaOH and yet no more soluble in NH_4OH than in water?

4. Show by formulating and combining the mass-action equation for the solubility-product of $Al(OH)_3$ dissociating as a base into Al^{+++} and OH^- ions and the mass-action equation for the formation of AlO_2^- out of Al^{+++} and OH^- ions that the quantity of aluminum dissolved (as AlO_2^-) in the presence of a base is proportional to the OH^- concentration in the solution.

5. Name all the elements that form ammonia complexes in all the groups thus far considered. What can be said as to the position of these elements in the periodic system? (Refer to a text-book of Inorganic Chemistry.)

6. If in an actual analysis no precipitate is obtained on the addition of NH_4OH, what conclusion may be drawn?

7. Which of the hydroxides precipitated by NH_4OH undergo no change on addition of $(NH_4)_2S$?

8. What must be the explanation of the facts that these trivalent hydroxides are not converted into sulfides and that the bivalent elements of these groups are precipitated as sulfides but not as hydroxides?

9. Which of the hydroxides precipitated by NaOH undergo change on the addition of Na_2O_2, and into what compound is each of these hydroxides converted?

10. What substances are produced by the action of Na_2O_2 on water?

Experiment 18. — *Analysis of the Aluminum-Group.* — 1. In separating the aluminum from the chromium and zinc with NH_4OH in P. 53, what would be the harm of adding too small an excess? What of adding too large an excess?

2. H_2SiO_3 (in hydrated form) dissolves somewhat in solutions of dilute acids and readily in those of largely ionized bases, but is precipitated from solutions with small concentrations of H^+ or OH^- ions (such as prevails in a solution of NH_4OH and ammonium salt). If H_2SiO_3 were present in the solution, state how it would behave in P. 51, 52, 53, and 54.

3. What is meant by adsorption? How is it illustrated in the confirmatory test for aluminum?

4. What is meant by a basic salt? Why is the precipitate produced by Na_2CO_3 with zinc salts called basic zinc carbonate? How is BiOCl related to a basic bismuth chloride?

5. In dissolving the sulfides in HCl and HNO_3 in P. 52 a little H_2SO_4 is usually formed. Would this be expected to have any effect on the test for chromate with $PbAc_2$ in P. 57?

6. Make a table (like that described in Question 1 on Expt. 8) showing the operations involved and the behavior of the chromium and zinc in analyzing a dilute HNO_3 solution of $ZnCrO_4$, beginning with the H_2S precipitation (P. 21) and continuing through the analysis of the aluminum-group (P. 51–57). At the foot of the table write all the chemical equations involved.

Experiments 19 and 20. — *Analysis of the Iron-Group.* — 1. What are the oxides of manganese corresponding to its three stages of oxidation occurring in P. 61 and 62? What is the valence of manganese in each of these oxides? How do they differ with respect to the formation of salts with acids and with bases?

2. Make a table (like that described in Question 1 on Expt. 8) showing the operations involved and the behavior of manganese in analyzing a dilute HNO_3 solution of $CaMnO_4$, beginning with the H_2S precipitation and continuing through the final test for manganese (thus involving P. 21, 51, 52, 61, and 62). Write also all the chemical equations involved.

3. Why is a large excess of NH_4OH added in precipitating the iron in P. 63?

4. Why is it necessary to test for zinc in the analysis of the iron-group?

5. Why may zinc be precipitated by NaOH and Na_2O_2 in the first treatment (in P. 52), and yet not be precipitated by them in the second treatment (in P. 66)?

6. When the original Na_2O_2 precipitate is so small that zinc need not be tested for in the iron-group, how may P. 66 be simplified?

7. What happens to $Zn(NO_3)_2$ and to $Co(NO_3)_2$ when they are ignited separately, and when an intimate mixture of them is ignited as in the confirmatory test for zinc?

8. Write the chemical equations expressing the steps by which $CoCl_2$ may be considered to be converted into $K_3Co(NO_2)_6$.

9. It is to be noted that cobalt is oxidized to the cobaltic state, even by fairly strong oxidizing agents like Na_2O_2 or HNO_2, only when there is produced a very slightly soluble cobaltic compound (such as $Co(OH)_3$ in the presence of $NaOH$), or a complex salt (like the cobaltinitrite). How must these conditions affect the concentration of the simple Co^{+++} ion in the solution? And how must this affect the reduction-potential of Co^{++}, Co^{+++}, and the tendency of cobalt to change from the cobaltous and to cobaltic state?

10. In what two ways may the fact that nickel is not oxidized under the same conditions be accounted for?

11. Name all the elements thus far considered which in any state of oxidation form colored compounds in solution. What can be said as to the position of these elements in the periodic system?

12. State how each of the following elements would behave if it were retained in the precipitate produced by H_2S in P. 21 and that precipitate were subjected to the Procedures for the analysis of the copper- and tin-groups: (a) iron; (b) aluminum; (c) zinc.

13. State how each of the following elements would behave if it remained in the filtrate from the H_2S precipitate and were subjected to the Procedures for the precipitation and analysis of the aluminum and iron groups: (a) copper; (b) lead; (c) arsenic. ($Cu(OH)_2$ is not soluble in an excess of $NaOH$; $Pb(OH)_2$ is soluble in excess of $NaOH$, but is converted into insoluble PbO_2 by Na_2O_2; lead is not precipitated as PbO_2 by $HClO_3$ in HNO_3 solution.)

Experiments 22 and 23. — *Analysis of the Aluminum- and Iron-Groups in the Presence of Phosphate.* — 1. What bearing would the fact that the original substance dissolved in water with a neutral or alkaline reaction to litmus have on the possibility of alkaline-earth elements being precipitated by NH_4OH when phosphate is present?

2. What difference would it make in this conclusion if the original substance dissolved in water with an acid reaction? Give an example of a solid substance or mixture containing alkaline-earth phosphate which would so dissolve.

3. If in P. 50 phosphate has been found present and in P. 51 NH_4OH has given a precipitate, explain whether it would be necessary to test for alkaline-earth elements in the filtrate from the $(NH_4)_2S$ precipitate.

4. If in P. 50 phosphate has been found present and in P. 51 NH_4OH produced no precipitate but $(NH_4)_2S$ did so, explain whether it would be necessary to provide for detecting alkaline-earth elements in the analysis of the iron-group. Name a substance or mixture which would conform to these conditions.

5. In the test for iron with $K_4Fe(CN)_6$ why must HNO_3 and Cl_2 first be removed by evaporation?

6. By formulating the mass-action expression for the hydrolysis of $FeAc_3$ show how the ratio of the concentration of $Fe(OH)_3$ to that of Fe^{+++} is related to the concentrations of HAc and Ac^- in the solution; and state what this shows as to the best conditions for securing complete precipitation of the iron. State what limitation makes somewhat difficult the realization of these conditions.

7. What must be the explanation of the fact that the phosphate combines with the ferric iron rather than with one of the bivalent elements when both are present?

8. Describe as in Question 1, Expt. 8, the behavior which a solution of $Ca_3(PO_4)_2$ in HNO_3 would show when submitted to the operations involved in the precipitation and separation of the aluminum and iron groups (P. 51–57, 61–68).

Experiment 25. — *Precipitation of the Alkaline-Earth Group.* — 1. What does this experiment show as to the precipitation by $(NH_4)_2CO_3$: (*a*) of magnesium, and (*b*) of the other alkaline-earth elements (which all behave like calcium)?

2. Why would a reagent consisting of NH_4HCO_3 not be suitable for the separation? Why is it advantageous to have more NH_3 present than corresponds to the neutral salt $(NH_4)_2CO_3$?

3. Why, in order to secure complete precipitation of the magnesium, is it necessary to shake the mixture and let it stand for a considerable time? Does this change the solubility of the precipitate?

4. To what is the action of the alcohol in diminishing the solubility primarily due — a change in ionization or a change in the medium as a solvent?

5. In some schemes of analysis $(NH_4)_2CO_3$ is used under other conditions for separating barium, strontium, and calcium from magnesium. What experiments would one make in developing such a procedure and testing its effectiveness?

Experiment 26. — *Analysis of the Alkaline-Earth Group.* — 1. In order to make a separation of 1 mg. of barium from 500 mg. of strontium, what must be the concentration of $CrO_4^=$, stated with reference to the saturation-values of the ion-concentration products of $BaCrO_4$ and $SrCrO_4$?

2. What would have to be true of the ratio of these two saturation-

values in order that this separation may be possible? What is the actual ratio of these two values? (See the Table of Solubilities in the Appendix.)

3. Write the mass-action expressions for the equilibrium of the reaction by which chromate-ion is converted into hydrochromate-ion, and of that by which hydrochromate-ion is converted into bichromate-ion. Show by these expressions what determines the relative proportions of the first two of these ions in any solution, and what determines the concentration of bichromate-ion in any solution.

4. In practice what three substances must be added in proper proportions in order to secure the right concentration of $CrO_4^=$ in the solution?

5. Why is the second K_2CrO_4 precipitate obtained in the confirmatory test for barium more conclusive evidence of its presence than the first K_2CrO_4 precipitate?

6. On addition of NH_4OH in P. 74 what chemical change causes the change in color from orange to yellow? Why from a mass-action standpoint does the addition of NH_4OH cause this change to take place? Why does this change cause strontium to precipitate?

7. Explain with reference to the saturation-values of the ion-concentration products why the carbonate-oxalate mixture used in P. 75 converts $SrCrO_4$ into $SrCO_3$ (rather than into SrC_2O_4), and $CaCrO_4$ into CaC_2O_4 (rather than into $CaCO_3$).

8. Why does the fact that MgC_2O_4 is a slightly ionized salt cause the presence of magnesium to diminish the delicacy of the oxalate test for calcium?

9. Why does CaC_2O_4 react with dilute H_2SO_4, but not with HAc?

10. How does the confirmatory test for calcium distinguish it from barium and strontium, which form much less soluble sulfates? How does it distinguish calcium from magnesium?

11. Could magnesium be precipitated by any other reagent in the form of a compound closely analogous to $MgNH_4PO_4$?

12. Why is the production of a precipitate with Na_2HPO_4 in the confirmatory test for magnesium (in P. 79) more conclusive evidence of its presence than the production of the first Na_2HPO_4 precipitate (in P. 78)?

13. How would each of the alkaline-earth elements behave in the subsequent Procedures of the group if the element were not completely precipitated in the proper place?

Experiments 27 and 28. — *Analysis of the Alkali-Group.* — 1. If the ammonium salt were not completely removed by the ignition, how would it behave in the subsequent tests for potassium?

2. Why is the separation of potassium and sodium by the $HClO_4$ method satisfactory when these elements are present as chlorides or nitrates, but not when they are present as sulfates? Why is it satisfactory when they are present as phosphates?

3. What is implied by the statement that $Na_3Co(NO_2)_6$ is a complex salt in solution?

4. How might a solution of $Na_3Co(NO_2)_6$ be prepared, judging from the experience previously obtained in the test for cobalt?

5. What are the formulas of antimonic acid and of the three salts of it that are theoretically possible? Explain the fact that only one hydrogen of antimonic acid is replaced by potassium or sodium even when an excess of KOH or NaOH is present.

Experiment 31. — *Determination of the State of Oxidation of Certain Elements forming Basic Constituents.* — 1. Make a table showing all of these elements which exist in two or more states of oxidation, the valence of these elements in each of these states, and the corresponding ions in the form of which the elements mainly exist in solution.

2. Show by the method described in the second paragraph of Note 10, P. 21, that the valences of the elements in the various anions included in the table are those attributed to the elements. Show whether or not chromium is in the same state of oxidation in $CrO_4^=$ and $Cr_2O_7^=$.

3. State what indications, if any, as to the state of oxidation of each of the elements existing in two or more states may be obtained during the course of the analysis for basic constituents.

DETECTION OF THE ACIDIC CONSTITUENTS

Experiment 33. — *Preparation of the Sodium Carbonate Solution.* — 1. State what action boiling Na_2CO_3 solution has on each of the following substances: $PbCl_2$, $Cu(AsO_2)_2$, $Al(OH)_3$, NH_4Cl, $CaCrO_4$, and CuS. Write the chemical equations involved.

2. Name the important kinds of substances that are not much acted upon by boiling Na_2CO_3 solution.

3. With the aid of the explanation and data given in Note 7, P. 101, calculate how many milligrams of $BaSO_4$ would actually be converted into $BaCO_3$ at 20° by 25 cc. of 3 n. Na_2CO_3 solution (assuming that the Na_2CO_3 and Na_2SO_4 in the solution have the same percentage ionization). Calculate how many milligrams would be converted if only the equivalent quantity of Na_2CO_3 were required.

4. With aid of the above explanation and the Table of Solubilities in the Appendix, calculate the equilibrium conditions that would result on treating $PbSO_4$ and $PbCrO_4$ with Na_2CO_3 solution at 20°. Predict whether in practice 2.5 g. of each of these salts would be completely or only partially decomposed by 25 cc. of 3 n. Na_2CO_3 solution.

5. Derive the mass-action expression (by a method like that used in Note 7, P. 101) for the equilibrium that would result when a slightly soluble salt with univalent anion (like AgCl) is treated with Na_2CO_3 solution.

6. With the aid of the result obtained in answering the preceding question and the solubility values involved, calculate the chloride-ion concentration that would result on treating an excess of AgCl with 3 n. Na_2CO_3 solution, taking the carbonate-ion concentration in the latter as 2 normal (or 2000 millinormal). Predict whether 2.5 g. of AgCl would be completely decomposed, considerably decomposed, or scarcely at all acted on by 25 cc. of 3 n. Na_2CO_3 solution at 20°.

Experiments 34 and 35. — *Detection of the Chloride-Group.* — 1. Arrange the silver salts of all the acidic constituents included in this System of Analysis in three groups comprising respectively: those very soluble in water; those only slightly soluble in water, but readily soluble in dilute HNO_3; and those only slightly soluble in dilute HNO_3.

2. Explain by reference to the solubilities of the salts and the ionizations of the corresponding acids why each of the salts in the second group referred to in the previous question dissolves in dilute HNO_3.

3. Explain why the silver halides do not dissolve in dilute HNO_3.

4. Explain why Ag_2S is only slightly soluble in dilute HNO_3, even though the ionization of HS^- is extremely small.

5. Explain why $Ag_2(CN)_2$ is only slightly soluble in dilute HNO_3, even though HCN is very slightly ionized.

D

6. If the $NaNO_2$ reagent contained chloride as an impurity, how could this be removed in a simple way that would not interfere with the use of the reagent for this test?

Experiment 36. — *Detection of the Sulfate-Group.* — 1. Arrange the barium salts of all the acidic constituents included in this System of Analysis in four groups comprising respectively: those very soluble in water; those only slightly soluble in water, but very soluble in HAc; those only slightly soluble in HAc, but very soluble in dilute HCl; and those only slightly soluble in dilute HCl.

2. What is the purpose of adding $CaCl_2$ solution with the $BaCl_2$ solution? What facts in regard to solubility make this addition necessary?

3. If the $CaCl_2$ reagent contained sulfate as an impurity, how could this be removed in a simple way that would not interfere with the use of the reagent for this test?

Experiment 37. — *Detection of Oxidizing and Reducing Constituents.* — 1. Write the chemical formulas of all the oxidizing acids which produce a dark color with the $MnCl_2$ reagent, and of the product to which each of these acids might be expected to be reduced by the reagent.

2. With the aid of the method described in Note 10, P. 21, write chemical equations expressing the action of each of these acids on $MnCl_2$.

3. Explain how the presence of sulfide (or other reducing constituent) in the substance might prevent the simultaneous presence of nitrate (or other oxidizing constituent) from being detected by the $MnCl_2$ test. State what relative molecular quantities of sulfide and nitrate would cause the $MnCl_2$ test to yield a positive result, and what would cause it to yield a negative result.

4. Write chemical equations expressing the action of each one of the reducing acids on $K_3Fe(CN)_6$, and that of H_2SO_3 on $Fe(NO_3)_3$.

Experiment 38. — *Identification of Acidic Constituents by the Group-Reagents.* — 1. Make a table showing, opposite the name of each one of the acidic constituents, its behavior toward each one of the four group-reagents.

2. Name all the acidic constituents that can be present in each of the following cases: (*a*) none of the four group-reagents gives a positive result; (*b*) the chloride-group reagent yields a precipitate, the sulfate-group reagent yields no precipitate, and oxidizing and reducing constituents are both found absent; (*c*) the chloride-group reagent yields no precipitate, the sulfate-group reagent produces a precipitate, oxidizing constituents are found absent, and reducing constituents are found present.

3. A solution known to contain only a single constituent gives a yellow chloride-group precipitate, a blue precipitate with the ferricyanide reagent, and negative results with the other two reagents. What constituent is present?

4. A solution known to contain only a single constituent gives a brown color with the $MnCl_2$ reagent, but negative results with the other three reagents. What constituent is present?

5. Explain how nitrite can act both as an oxidizing and a reducing constituent.

Experiment 39. — *Analysis of the Chloride-Group.* — 1. With the aid of the Table of Solubilities in the Appendix predict what constituents beside sulfide might be precipitated on the addition of $Pb(NO_3)_2$ to the Na_2CO_3 solution, wholly or in part. Explain whether this is determined solely by the relative solubilities of $PbCO_3$ and the other lead salts in water.

2. Explain whether the $Pb(NO_3)_2$ could be replaced by $AgNO_3$.

3. Explain the fact that no HCN is set free on acidifying solutions of $Na_3Fe(CN)_6$ and $Na_4Fe(CN)_6$.

4. Suggest possible explanations of the fact that $Ni(CN)_2$ is only slightly soluble in HAc.

5. The reducing constituents tested for in P. 105 all reduce $HClO_3$ in a strongly acid solution. Of these constituents what ones might be used in place of HNO_2 in testing for chlorate in P. 108?

Experiment 41. — *Detection of Thiocyanate and the Different Halides.* — 1. Derive, in the way described in Note 3, P. 110, the relation stated in that Note to exist between the solubilities in water and those in dilute NH_4OH of slightly soluble silver salts.

2. A saturated solution of AgCl in 2 n. NH_4OH at 25° is 0.15 normal. With the aid of the principle considered in the preceding question, calculate approximately how many milligrams of iodine as AgI, and of bromine as AgBr, would be dissolved by that quantity of 2 n. NH_4OH required to dissolve 210 mg. of chlorine as AgCl. State whether a good analytical separation of any two of these three acidic constituents could be based on the difference in the solubilities of the silver salts in NH_4OH.

3. With the aid of the values of the molal reduction-potentials given in the Table in the Appendix explain why $Fe(NO_3)_3$ liberates I_2 from an iodide almost completely, but sets free scarcely any Br_2 from a bromide.

4. Predict whether any reaction would occur, and whether or not it would be practically complete, on mixing the following substances (the halogen being in moderate excess): (*a*) Br_2 and KCl; (*b*) Br_2 and KI; (*c*) Cl_2 and KBr; (*d*) Cl_2 and $FeCl_2$; (*e*) I_2 and FeI_2.

5. If 100 mg. of I_2 were present in 10 cc. of solution, what quantity of it would remain in the aqueous layer after it was shaken with 1 cc. of CCl_4? After it was shaken a second time with 1 cc. of CCl_4? After it was shaken a third time with 1 cc. of CCl_4? What quantity would remain in the aqueous layer if it were shaken at first with 3 cc. of CCl_4?

6. If 100 mg. of Br_2 were present in 10 cc. of solution, what quantity of it would remain in the aqueous layer after it was shaken with 1 cc. of CCl_4?

7. Explain why the time required for liberating the bromine from a bromide by $KMnO_4$ would be diminished much more by doubling the concentration of the HNO_3 than by doubling that of the $KMnO_4$.

8. Write the equation expressing the formation of MnO_2 by the action of $KMnO_4$ on HBr; also the equation expressing the action of HNO_2 on MnO_2 in HNO_3 solution.

9. What error might result if the mixture were not boiled long enough before adding the $NaNO_2$ and $AgNO_3$? What test might be made before adding these reagents, to guard against this error?

Experiment 44. — *Analysis of the Sulfate-Group.* — 1. Explain with the aid of the solubilities of the salts involved whether sulfide could be removed in this case, as in P. 106, by adding $Pb(NO_3)_2$ to the Na_2CO_3 solution and filtering the mixture before acidifying it.

2. Why must sulfide and thiocyanate be removed before testing for sulfite?

3. By considering the ionization and solubility values involved, explain why $BaSO_3$ and $BaCrO_4$ are not precipitated in the presence of HCl, but are so precipitated when only HAc is present; and why $BaHPO_4$ is not precipitated even in the presence of HAc.

4. State and explain with reference to the solubility and ionization values involved how fluoride behaves in each step of P. 111.

5. Make a similar statement and explanation as to how oxalate would behave in P. 111.

6. Suggest a reason why chromate, though it is one of the constituents of the sulfate-group, is not included in the mixture (of Na_2S, Na_2SO_4, Na_2SO_3, and NaF) used in illustrating the method of analysis of that group.

7. Write the chemical equations expressing all the successive reactions involved in treating CaF_2 by the confirmatory test for fluoride (P. 112).

Experiment 45. — *Detection of Nitrate or Nitrite.* — 1. Write the chemical equations expressing the action of Al on $NaOH$ solution, and that of the hydrogen thereby produced on $NaNO_2$ and $NaNO_3$.

2. State why cyanides and thiocyanate must be removed before carrying out this Procedure; and explain with reference to the solubilities of the silver salts involved why they can be removed by adding Ag_2CO_3 to the Na_2CO_3 solution.

Experiment 50. — *Detection of Sulfate, Carbonate, Sulfide, and Cyanide.* — 1. Describe how sulfite would interfere with the test for carbonate in P. 117. State how a precipitate of $BaSO_3$ would be distinguished from one of $BaCO_3$. Explain how the addition of H_2O_2, directed in Note 2, P. 117, removes the difficulty of detecting carbonate in the presence of sulfite.

2. Write chemical equations expressing the action of Zn and HCl on CuS, As_2S_3, FeS_2, and $PbSO_4$.

3. Write the chemical equations expressing all the successive reactions in the test for cyanide in P. 121.

Experiment 51. — *Detection of Chloride, Fluoride, and Borate.* — 1. State what influence the presence of much silica in the substance would have on the detection of fluoride in P. 122.

2. By considering the ionization-values involved, state to what extent HBO_2 is displaced from borates by H_2SO_4; and explain why it does not pass over into the distillate till CH_3OH is added.

PREPARATION OF THE SOLUTION FOR THE DETECTION OF BASIC CONSTITUENTS AND THE COMPLETE ANALYSIS OF UNKNOWN SUBSTANCES

Experiment 52. — *Indications of Certain Constituents Afforded by the Closed-Tube Test.* — 1. Of what elements are organic substances (carbon-containing compounds) most commonly composed, and what causes them to blacken on heating?

2. Explain whether the presence of a large quantity of sugar in a substance would interfere with the precipitation of the copper- and tin-groups, with that of the aluminum- and iron-groups, and with that of the alkaline-earth group; also whether its presence would interfere with the detection of the alkali-elements.

3. Name the different forms in which water may be present in a substance.

4. If a substance were ignited at a red heat (for example, to destroy organic matter) before submitting it to analysis, what basic constituents would be lost?

5. State how each of the following substances would behave in the closed-tube test, and write the chemical equation expressing the reaction that takes place: $MgNH_4PO_4$, $KHSO_4$, $PbCO_3$, $KClO_3$, As_2O_3.

Experiment 53. — *Analysis of Non-Metallic Substances Dissolved by Water or Dilute Acid.* — 1. Tabulate the behavior shown by each of the following substances when treated with water, tested with litmus, and treated with 2 n. HNO_3, cold and hot, as directed in P. 2: $Bi(NO_3)_3$, $FeCO_3$, Na_2SiO_3, KI, CdS, KCN, $KAg(CN)_2$, $Ca_3(PO_4)_2$, $BaSO_3$, $SnCl_2$.

2. What determines whether a sodium salt is hydrolyzed so as to give an alkaline reaction to litmus, and what determines whether a nitrate is hydrolyzed so as to give an acid reaction to litmus?

Experiment 54. — *Analysis of Non-Metallic Substances Dissolved only by Concentrated Acids.* — 1. What acidic constituent forms salts many of which are not dissolved by cold dilute HNO_3, but are decomposed by hot concentrated HNO_3 because of its oxidizing action?

2. State what happens (that is, what chemical changes occur and what phenomena are observed) at each step of the process when each of the following substances is treated by P. 3 : $CuSiO_3$ (a silicate decomposed by acids), Sb_2S_3, MnO_2, $PbCrO_4$, $PbSO_4$, Ag_3PO_4, HgS, Hg_2Cl_2, Fe_3O_4.

3. Give examples of substances which dissolve in the acids used in P. 3 in virtue (*a*) of the action of the acids as such; (*b*) of the oxidizing action, and (*c*) of the reducing action.

Experiment 55. — *Analysis of Alloys.* — 1. What elements are scarcely ever found in alloys, and how in consequence may the analysis of an alloy be shortened?

2. State the result of treating, as in P. 4, each of the following alloys, (*a*) with 6 n. HNO_3, and (*b*) with 6 n. HCl (after adding HCl and evaporating the mixture) : brass (Cu, Zn) ; solder (Pb, Sn) ; ferrosilicon (Fe, Si, C) ; coin-silver (Ag, Cu).

Experiment 56. — *Analysis of Natural Substances or Igneous Products Not Completely Dissolved by Treatment with Nitric and Hydrochloric Acids.* — 1. State what happens to each of the substances whose symbols are given under (*b*) in Table I when it is treated as in P. 5 : (*a*) with concentrated H_2SO_4 ; (*b*) then with HF ; (*c*) then (after evaporating) with dilute H_2SO_4. State also what happens on treating with Na_2CO_3 solution by P. 6 any residue undissolved by the dilute H_2SO_4.

2. State what happens to feldspar (potassium aluminum silicate, an example of a silicate not much decomposed by acids other than HF) when it is treated by P. 5.

3. State what happens to each of the substances whose symbols are given under (*b*) in Table I (including also feldspar as an example of a silicate) on fusing it with Na_2CO_3 and $NaNO_3$, on treating the fused mass with water, and on treating the residue with dilute HNO_3, as described in P. 7.

4. State on which of these substances the $NaNO_3$ added in the fusion has an effect, and what that effect is in each case.

Thursday
1/14/3v
topage 58
See Back
of Lab. Note
Book.

PART II

THE SYSTEM OF ANALYSIS

PREPARATION OF THE SOLUTION

FOR THE

DETECTION OF THE BASIC CONSTITUENTS

GENERAL DIRECTIONS

Procedure 1. — *Preliminary Examination and General Directions.* — In case the substance is a non-metallic solid, note its color, odor, and texture; examine it with a lens to determine whether it is heterogeneous, and, if so, note the appearance of its constituents. To determine whether organic matter or water is present and to get other indications, heat gently at first, then strongly, about 0.1 cc. of the finely powdered substance in a hard-glass tube (of about 10 mm. bore and 100 mm. length) closed at one end. Note whether the substance blackens, whether a tarry, aqueous, or other deposit forms on the cold part of the tube, and whether any odor is emitted.

If organic matter is thus proved absent, prepare a solution of the substance by treating a sample of it by P. 2–3 and P. 5–6 (or 7). If organic matter is proved present, treat the substance by P. 8. Treat the so-prepared solution or solutions as directed in these Procedures, to detect basic constituents.

Treat fresh samples of the substance by P. 91 to detect ammonium, and by P. 92, if necessary, to determine the state of oxidation of certain basic constituents.

Treat fresh samples of the substance as directed in P. 100, to detect acidic constituents.

39

In case the substance is an alloy, prepare a solution of it by P. 4, and analyze this solution by P. 21–79.   If there is a residue, treat it by P. 5, followed by P. 11–68.

In case the substance is a solution, treat it as directed in P. 9.

Notes. — 1. When a complete analysis in the wet way is to be made, it is usually not worth while to make a more extended preliminary examination in the dry way.   The closed-tube test is, however, essential, in order to show whether organic matter is present; for certain kinds of organic matter, especially sugars and hydroxy-acids, such as tartaric, citric, and lactic acids, prevent the precipitation of the hydroxides of most of the elements by alkalies.   Such organic matter must therefore be detected and removed in order to insure the precipitation of aluminum and chromium by NH_4OH.   Moreover, a large quantity of organic matter of any kind interferes with the execution of the analysis; for example, with the operations of solution, filtration, and evaporation. Alloys do not contain organic matter or water; therefore the closed-tube test need not be applied to them.

2. Blackening accompanied by a burnt odor or by the formation of a tarry deposit shows organic matter.   Blackening alone does not show it; for copper, cobalt, and nickel salts may turn black on heating, owing to the formation of the black oxides.   Oxalates blacken and emit a burnt odor to a much less extent than other organic substances, and may not be detected by the closed-tube test.

3. It is usually desirable to determine whether water is a constituent of the substance, and, if so, whether it is present in large or small proportion.   This can be done with a fair degree of delicacy by the closed-tube test, provided care be taken to keep the upper part of the tube cool during the first of the heating.   Water may be present as so-called water of constitution, as in FeO_3H_3 or Na_2HPO_4; as water of crystallization, as in $MgSO_4 \cdot 7\,H_2O$; as inclosed water, as in some hydrated silicates like the zeolites or as mother-liquor within crystals; and as hygroscopic moisture on the surface.   Water of constitution may be expelled only at a fairly high temperature, while in the other forms it is seldom retained above 200°.

4. The closed-tube test may also furnish evidence of the presence of certain basic and acidic constituents when they are present in considerable quantity.   Thus all ammonium salts and mercury compounds are volatilized much below a red heat.   Ammonium salts and the chlorides of mercury give a white sublimate.   Most other mercury compounds give a gray one, consisting of minute globules of mercury, made visible

by a lens or by rubbing with a wire.   Metallic As, As_2O_3, and As_2S_3 are also readily volatilized, forming black, white, and yellow sublimates, respectively.   Of the acid-forming elements or groups, free sulfur or a persulfide is shown by a sublimate of reddish-brown drops, changing to a yellow solid on cooling, and accompanied by odor of SO_2; a moist sulfide, by the odor of H_2S; a nitrate or nitrite, by brown vapors of NO_2; free iodine or a decomposable iodide, by a black sublimate of I_2 and by its violet vapor; a sulfite, by the odor of SO_2; a peroxide, chlorate, or nitrate, by evolution of oxygen, recognized by its inflaming a glowing wood-splinter held in the tube; and a carbonate or oxalate, by the evolution of CO_2, recognized by its causing turbidity in a drop of $Ba(OH)_2$ solution.

PREPARATION OF THE SOLUTION FOR THE DETECTION OF BASIC
CONSTITUENTS

TABLE I. — PREPARATION OF THE SOLUTION IN THE CASE OF NON-
METALLIC SOLID SUBSTANCES FREE FROM ORGANIC MATTER

Heat the substance with water and dilute HNO_3 (P. 2).

A. It all dissolves. *Treat the solution by P. 11.*	B. It does not all dissolve.
	Residue:* (a) Sb_2O_5, H_2SnO_3, Fe_2O_3, MnO_2, PbO_2, S, many sulfides, $BaCrO_4$,$PbCrO_4$. (b) C, SiC, Al_2O_3, Cr_2O_3, AgCl, CaF_2, $CaSO_4$, $PbSO_4$, $BaSO_4$, $SrSO_4$, SnS_2, SnO_2, SiO_2, and many silicates.
	Solution: most substances as nitrates.
	Without filtering, evaporate the mixture to 2 cc., add HCl, evaporate completely, heat with dilute HCl, and filter the hot mixture (P. 3).

	Solution: *Treat by P. 21.*	Residue: substances under (b). *Heat with H_2SO_4 and HF, evaporate, add dilute H_2SO_4, boil (P. 5).*	
		Gas: SiF_4.	Residue: Pb, Ba, Sr, Ca, Cr, as sulfates. *Treat by P. 6.*	Solution: Other elements as sulfates. *Treat by P. 11.*

* Only the more common substances that are likely to be present in the residue are here mentioned; and some of these may pass wholly or partially into the solution.

Procedure 2. — *Treatment of Non-Metallic Substances Free from Organic Matter.* — Weigh out on a rough balance 1 g. of the finely powdered substance (see Note 1), add to it in a conical flask 10 cc. of water, heat the mixture to boiling if there is a residue, and test the solution with litmus paper. Add to the mixture, if it is not already acid, 6 n. HNO_3, a few drops at a time, till, after shaking, it becomes distinctly acid. Note whether there is an odor or effervescence. Then cool the mixture, and add to it, without filtering out any residue, just 5 cc. of 6 n. HNO_3. If there is a residue (but not otherwise), heat the mixture nearly to boiling for 2 or 3 minutes, covering the flask with a watch-glass and not letting the mixture actually boil. Cool the mixture.

In case a clear solution results, treat it by P. 11.

In case the substance dissolves completely in the hot acid but a precipitate separates on cooling, filter, treat the filtrate by P. 11, reserve the precipitate (without washing it), and add it later to the solution to be treated by P. 21.

In case the substance does not dissolve completely even in the hot acid, treat the mixture without filtering it by P. 3.

> *Notes.* — 1. Before treating the substance with solvents it is reduced to an impalpable powder by grinding it, a little at a time, in a porcelain or agate mortar; for this greatly hastens the solution of slowly dissolving substances. With hard substances, and in general with minerals, an agate mortar is used; but as this may be broken by a blow, the substance must be ground, not pounded, in it.
>
> 2. The quantity of the substance taken for analysis should always be approximately known; for a good qualitative analysis should not only show the presence or absence of the various elements in the substance, but should enable their relative quantities to be estimated. Since 1 or 2 mg. of almost any element can be detected by this system of analysis, the presence of 0.1–0.2% of an element will be detected when one gram of substance is taken, and this degree of delicacy is ordinarily sufficient. If much more than this quantity is taken, the precipitates may be so large that much time is consumed in filtering and washing them. Moreover, the directions for many of the separations are not satisfactory when more than 500 mg. of any one constituent is present.
>
> 3. The substance is treated with only 10 cc. of water so that the HNO_3 subsequently added may be concentrated enough to prevent the hydrolysis of salts of bismuth, antimony, and tin, and thus insure their solution. The mixture is cooled before the addition of the main quantity of HNO_3 so as to avoid oxidizing mercurous, arsenous, and ferrous salts unnecessarily. But, in case there is a residue, the mixture is heated, since the hot acid, largely owing to its oxidizing action, has a greater solvent effect on many substances, notably on sulfides.
>
> 4. To what extent the substance dissolves in water and in dilute HNO_3 should be noted, since it furnishes important indications of the nature of the constituents present. General statements as to the solubilities of chemical substances in water and dilute acid will be found in the Appendix under " Solubilities." When, however, the substance to be analyzed dissolves only partly in the water or in the dilute HNO_3, it is usually not worth while to filter off the residue and analyze it and the solution separately. This need be done only when knowledge is desired as to the water-soluble and acid-soluble constituents.

5. The residue undissolved by HNO_3 probably consists of one or more of the substances whose formulas are given in Table I under (*a*) and (*b*). Some of these substances (for example, Fe_2O_3 and Al_2O_3) are really soluble in the acid; but, when in the form of native or ignited products, they may fail to dissolve because of a very slow rate of solution. Other less common substances that may be present in the residue are anhydrous chromium salts, stannic phosphate, and the ferrocyanides of iron and of some other elements.

6. Just 5 cc. of 6 n. HNO_3 are added at this point, in order that the acid concentration may be properly adjusted in the subsequent H_2S precipitation. For this reason, when the solution is alkaline or when a substance (like an undissolved oxide or carbonate) which neutralizes the acid is present, the solution is made distinctly acid before adding the 5 cc. of HNO_3. For the same reason care is taken to prevent loss of the acid by evaporation.

7. If the aqueous solution has an alkaline reaction, the addition of an acid may cause precipitation of any substance held in solution by an alkaline solvent; for example, sulfur or sulfides of the tin-group from an alkaline sulfide solution; silver chloride or cyanide from a potassium cyanide solution; silicic acid from sodium silicate solution; or basic hydroxides from solutions in alkalies. These last substances redissolve when the excess of HNO_3 is added.

8. An acid reaction of the aqueous solution towards litmus is due to hydrogen-ion, which may arise from free acid, from an acid salt of a strong acid, or (by hydrolysis) from a neutral salt of a strong acid and a weak base. An alkaline reaction is due to hydroxide-ion, which may arise from a soluble hydroxide, or (by hydrolysis) from a carbonate, sulfide, phosphate, borate, cyanide, or a salt of some other weak acid.

9. When the acid is added to the aqueous solution, the evolution of any gas and its odor should be noted, since this indicates the nature of the acidic constituents present. Thus carbonates effervesce with evolution of CO_2; sulfides produce the odor of H_2S; sulfites and thiosulfates, that of SO_2; and cyanides, that of HCN.

10. On heating the HNO_3 solution, sulfur may separate as a spongy or pasty mass, indicating the presence of sulfide; iodine may be liberated from an iodide, producing a black precipitate, a brown color in the solution, or violet vapors above it; bromine may be set free from a bromide, yielding a red solution; nitrogen peroxide may be produced by action of the HNO_3 on a sulfide, sulfite, or iodide, or on a mercurous, stannous, or ferrous compound; silicic acid may be set free as a gelatinous precipitate, indicating the presence of a decomposable silicate; and a white amorphous precipitate of antimonic oxide (Sb_2O_5) or metastannic acid (H_2SnO_3) may separate.

Procedure 3. — *Further Treatment of Non-Metallic Substances Not Dissolved by Dilute Nitric Acid.* — In case the substance has not dissolved in dilute HNO_3, transfer the unfiltered mixture (P. 2) to a casserole, evaporate it to about 2 cc., add 5 cc. of 12 n. HCl, and evaporate slowly just to dryness.

Heat the residue carefully at 100–130° till it is dry, keeping the casserole in motion over a small flame. Loosen the residue from the dish, and rub it to a fine powder with a pestle; add to it just 5 cc. of 6 n. HCl, cover the dish, and warm the mixture, taking care that none of the acid evaporates. Add 10 cc. of water to the mixture, and heat it just to boiling. (If there is a residue that seems to be gradually dissolving, add 2 cc. of 12 n. HCl, evaporate the mixture slowly almost to dryness, and heat the moist residue with 5 cc. of 6 n. HCl and 10 cc. of water, as before.) Filter the boiling-hot mixture. Treat the filtrate by P. 21. Wash the residue with 5–10 cc. of 2 n. HCl and then thoroughly with hot water (rejecting all the washings), and treat it by P. 5 (or by P. 7 in case the use of a platinum crucible or of hydrofluoric acid is impracticable).

Notes. — 1. The concentrating of the HNO_3 solution and the subsequent addition of HCl to it produce a strongly oxidizing solvent, which dissolves all sulfides (except ignited SnS_2). The mixture of HNO_3 and HCl, which is known as *aqua regia*, owes its powerful oxidizing action to the fact that these acids react with each other, when warm and concentrated, with the formation of Cl_2 and NOCl (nitrosyl chloride).

2. Enough HCl is added to destroy finally all the HNO_3. The concentrated HCl remaining then exercises a reducing action on such substances as MnO_2, PbO_2, $PbCrO_4$, and $BaCrO_4$, whereby they are converted into soluble compounds.

3. The hot concentrated HCl acts, moreover, as a powerful acid solvent on slowly dissolving oxides, such as Sb_2O_5, SnO_2, Fe_2O_3, Al_2O_3. Its action in this respect is far more rapid and effective than that of HNO_3. To allow time for it to act, it is directed that the acid be evaporated slowly.

4. It will be seen from the foregoing statements that, by using the two acids in the way directed in the Procedure, three types of solvent action are secured. The important substances which may resist this

treatment are those whose formulas are given in Table 1 under (*b*). Of these substances $CaSO_4$ and CaF_2 dissolve in considerable quantity, and $SrSO_4$ and $PbSO_4$ in small quantity, in the dilute HCl. The slightly soluble sulfates may not have been present in the original substance, but may have been produced by oxidation from some sulfide when the corresponding basic elements are also present.

5. Provided the substance has been treated by this Procedure, all the silver originally present, whatever may have been its form, will be left in the residue as AgCl. Any mercury, arsenic, antimony, tin, or iron present in the solution will be in the higher state of oxidation; any chromium will be in the form of chromic chloride, and any manganese in the form of manganous chloride.

6. When a silicate is decomposed by acid, silicic acid may separate as a gelatinous precipitate, but even then a part of it always remains in solution, mainly as a colloid. When thoroughly dried at $100\text{--}130°$, it is partially dehydrated and becomes entirely insoluble in acid. The HCl solution is therefore evaporated to dryness and the residue is heated at $100\text{--}130°$, in order to remove the silica at this point; for, if it were not removed, it would appear as a gelatinous precipitate at some later stage of the analysis; thus, if it did not separate earlier, it would be precipitated by NH_4OH with the aluminum and iron groups, and might then be mistaken for $Al(OH)_3$. Care is taken to avoid overheating, since it may cause other substances to dissolve only very slowly in dilute acid and may cause volatilization of mercury and tin. If the substance cannot contain silica, the heating may be omitted.

7. The foregoing statements show that, when no residue is left undissolved by the dilute HCl, silver, silica, and silicate can be pronounced absent; but that this is not true of any other constituent.

8. The concentrated HCl is completely removed by evaporation, the dried residue is treated with just 5 cc. of 6 n. HCl, care is taken to prevent evaporation of the acid, and the acid washings are not collected with the filtrate, so as to enable the acid concentration to be properly adjusted in the subsequent precipitation with H_2S.

9. Only 10 cc. of water are added to the HCl solution so that the acid may be concentrated enough to hold in solution even 500 mg. of bismuth and as much antimony as possible (about 60 mg.). The mixture is filtered boiling-hot so that lead may pass into the filtrate (which it does up to about 200 mg.). The residue is washed first with 2 n. HCl to remove bismuth and antimony salts, and then with hot water to remove other soluble substances, including any $PbCl_2$ present.

10. To avoid underestimating the quantity of antimony, it is well to add the HCl washings to ten volumes of water, whereupon SbOCl precipitates if more than about 60 mg. of antimony are present.

Procedure 4. — *Treatment of Alloys.* — In case the substance is an alloy, convert it into a form offering a large surface (see Note 1), and treat 0.5 g. of it in a casserole with 5 cc. of 6 n. HNO₃. Cover the dish with a watch-glass, and heat the mixture nearly to boiling so long as any action continues, adding 1 cc. of 16 n. HNO₃ if any of the alloy is still unattacked; evaporate to about 2 cc., add 5 cc. of 12 n. HCl, and evaporate slowly just to dryness. Treat the residue as directed in the last paragraph of P. 3, omitting the heating at 100–130° except in the case of iron alloys.

Notes. — 1. Many alloys cannot be powdered by grinding in a porcelain or agate mortar. They may usually be converted into a form that offers a large surface by hammering in a steel mortar, filing with fine steel file, shaving with a knife, or converting into turnings with a lathe. Only 0.5 g. of an alloy is taken for analysis; for, owing to the absence of acidic constituents, the same quantity of basic elements is contained in a smaller amount of substance.

2. Most alloys are attacked by strong HNO₃, all the elements that may be present going into solution, except antimony, tin, carbon, and silicon. Antimony is oxidized to antimonic oxide (Sb_2O_5), tin to metastannic acid (nH_2SnO_3), and silicon wholly or in part to silicic acid (H_2SiO_3); all of which substances separate as white amorphous precipitates when they are present in considerable quantity. Some nitrates, especially that of lead, may separate in crystalline form as the acid becomes concentrated.

3. The HCl added serves, both because of the formation of *aqua regia* and because of its own specific action, to bring into solution certain alloys, especially those of iron and of aluminum, which are only slowly attacked by HNO₃. The HCl also dissolves any oxide of antimony or of tin which may have been produced by the HNO₃. It may cause the precipitation of lead and silver as chlorides.

4. The heating of the dry residue at 100–130° serves to dehydrate silicic acid and make it insoluble in acid. This heating may ordinarily be omitted except in the case of iron alloys, since these are the only alloys likely to contain silica.

5. A residue undissolved by the dilute HCl may consist of silica, silicon, carbon, or silver chloride, or of certain alloys, like ferrochrome or ferrosilicon, which are only slowly attacked by HNO₃ and HCl. The residue is treated with HF and H_2SO_4 by P. 5 to detect and remove silica and to bring the other substances into solution.

6. The statements in Notes 5–9, P. 3, are applicable also to alloys.

Procedure 5. — *Treatment of the Residue with Hydrofluoric Acid.* — Transfer the residue undissolved by acids (P. 3 or 4) to a platinum or palladium-gold crucible (see Notes 1 and 2). Add to it just 3 cc. of 18 n. H_2SO_4, heat the crucible with a moving flame till thick white fumes begin to be given off, and let it cool completely.

To test for silicate, add carefully from a lead tube or hard-rubber tube capped with a rubber nipple pure 48% HF drop by drop until 5–6 drops have been added, and warm the mixture over a steam-bath. (Formation of gas bubbles, presence of SILICA or SILICATE.)

Then add 2–5 cc. more pure 48% HF, place the cover on the crucible, and digest the mixture on a steam-bath for about 15 minutes unless the residue dissolves more quickly; remove the cover; evaporate the mixture under a hood till white fumes of H_2SO_4 begin to be given off, taking care to avoid spattering (see Note 3); and let the crucible cool. In case there is a residue or precipitate, treat the mixture as described in the next paragraph. In case there is no residue or precipitate, evaporate the mixture under a hood just to dryness, taking care to avoid spattering and overheating (see Note 3). If there is now no residue (or only an insignificant one), proceed no further. If there is a considerable residue, cool the crucible, add to it just 3 cc. of 18 n. H_2SO_4, heat it slowly till the acid begins to fume (not allowing much of it to evaporate), cool the crucible, and treat the mixture as described in the next paragraph.

Pour the contents of the crucible into 15 cc. of water, rinsing out the crucible with the resulting solution. Boil the mixture gently for 4 to 5 minutes, or so long as the residue seems to be dissolving; filter, and wash the residue with 1 n. H_2SO_4, rejecting the washings. Treat the solution by P. 11–89, with such modifications as are justified by the knowledge that lead, barium, and strontium are not present in it. Treat the residue by P. 6 in case it came from a non-metallic substance; or by P. 7 in case it came from an alloy (see note 10).

Notes. — 1. *A student using this procedure for the first time should work under the direct supervision of an instructor. Great care must be taken not to breathe the fumes of HF nor to get it on the hands; for it is extremely irritating and produces dangerous burns.*

2. *Whenever a residue or precipitate has to be transferred from a filter to a crucible in which it is to be ignited or fused, it is best to roll up the part of the filter-paper to which most of the residue adheres, wind a platinum wire around it in the form of a spiral, dry it by holding it above a small gas-flame, and then heat it with a slanting flame till the carbon is all burnt off, holding the filter and residue constantly over the crucible placed on a watch-glass.*

3. *When a liquid is to be evaporated in a crucible, it is well to heat it within a larger iron crucible, which serves as an air-bath. The smaller crucible may be supported upon a nichrome triangle set into holes bored in the side of the iron crucible, or upon a circular disk of asbestos-board with a round hole cut out in the middle and slots cut out along the sides.*

4. The test for silica or silicate depends on the formation of SiF_4 gas, which is insoluble in strong H_2SO_4, but dissolves in water in the presence of HF with formation of fluosilicic acid, H_2SiF_6. With free silica the evolution of gas takes place in the cold; but with slowly decomposing silicates, such as feldspar, the test is obtained only upon warming. A few silicates are not acted upon by HF and H_2SO_4, and, of course, do not show the test for silica at this point. The test is delicate enough to enable 1 mg. of silica, whether free or in a decomposable silicate, to be detected. Moreover, after the substance has been treated with acids as in P. 3 or 4 and heated with H_2SO_4, an evolution of gas with HF is not produced with the compounds of any element other than silicon. It should be borne in mind that a small quantity of silica will be introduced if ordinary filters (which have not been washed with HF) have been employed and have been destroyed by acids or by ignition, or if a strongly alkaline solution has been boiled in glass vessels.

5. Since glass and porcelain consist of silicates which are readily attacked by HF, this acid must not be allowed to come into contact with these materials. In handling cold HF solutions, vessels and funnels of celluloid or paraffin or of glass coated with paraffin may be used; but platinum or palladium-gold vessels must be employed when the solutions are to be heated. Care must be taken not to introduce into a platinum or palladium-gold vessel any solution containing chlorine or bromine or any acid mixture containing nitrates and chlorides by which chlorine would be evolved. Platinum is so slowly attacked by hot concentrated H_2SO_4 that even when 2–3 cc. of the acid are rapidly evaporated in a crucible less than 0.5 mg. passes into solution.

E

6. The digestion with HF decomposes most silicates and dissolves silica. The subsequent evaporation with H_2SO_4 expels the excess of HF and decomposes the fluorides produced, as well as some other substances that may have been left undissolved by the HNO_3 and HCl.

7. In case there is no residue or precipitate after evaporating off the HF and cooling the remaining H_2SO_4, the residue undissolved by dilute HCl (in P. 3 or 4) may have consisted only of silica, sulfur, or carbon; in which case it is unnecessary to analyze the H_2SO_4 solution further. To determine this, the H_2SO_4 is completely evaporated off; and, if there is still no solid residue, it proves that the solution contains no basic constituents.

8. Just 3 cc. of 18 n. H_2SO_4 are added and the acid is not allowed to evaporate in the subsequent heating, so as to enable the acid concentration to be properly adjusted in the subsequent H_2S precipitation. This quantity of H_2SO_4 (54 milliequivalents) is made somewhat larger than the quantity (30 milliequivalents) of HNO_3 or HCl added in P. 2, 3, or 4, in order to allow for some loss in the evaporation and for the smaller degree of ionization of HSO_4^-. Only 15 cc. of water are added, so as to prevent the precipitation of antimony and bismuth as oxysalts, and so as to cause the complete precipitation of lead, barium, and strontium as sulfates. The solution is boiled so as to dissolve anhydrous sulfates, especially those of iron and aluminum. The residue is washed with 1 n. H_2SO_4 so that $PbSO_4$ and $SrSO_4$ may not be dissolved.

9. The residue undissolved by dilute H_2SO_4 contains as sulfates all of any barium, strontium, or lead, and nearly all of any calcium or chromium that remained in the residue from the treatments with HNO_3 and HCl. The chromium may be present because it is converted into an anhydrous, slowly dissolving sulfate. The residue may also contain some bismuth as basic sulfate, and some antimony as antimonic oxide. In it may also be present still undecomposed substances, especially the following: silver chloride; corundum (Al_2O_3); chromite, ($FeCr_2O_4$); cassiterite (SnO_2); some anhydrous silicates, such as cyanite or andalusite (Al_2SiO_5) and tourmalin; graphite and carborundum (SiC).

10. In the case of an alloy any residue undissolved by the dilute H_2SO_4 probably consists only of graphite, or of some of the silver chloride, chromium sulfate, or original alloy which has escaped decomposition. If black, it may be tested for graphite by drying it and rubbing it on the fingers or on paper. Unless it seems to consist wholly of graphite, it is treated by P. 7, and the solutions thus obtained are tested only for silver and chromium.

11. If the use of a platinum or a palladium-gold crucible or of hydrofluoric acid is impracticable, the residue insoluble in HCl may be fused in a nickel crucible with Na_2CO_3, as described in P. 7, instead of being treated by P. 5–6. This is, however, a far less satisfactory method of analysis for the following reasons. Compounds of the alkali elements are used as a flux, nickel is introduced from the crucible, and mercury compounds are volatilized; so these elements cannot be tested for in the subsequent analysis. Moreover, the treatment with HF and H_2SO_4 is almost always a shorter process, since when the residue consists only of silica, as is often the case with minerals, no further treatment is necessary, and since in other cases there is often no residue to be boiled with Na_2CO_3 solution (P. 6).

Procedure 6. — *Treatment of the Residue from the Fluoride Treatment.* — Transfer the residue undissolved by dilute H_2SO_4 (P. 5) to a casserole, add about 25 cc. of 3 n. Na_2CO_3 solution, cover the casserole, and boil gently for 10 minutes. Filter and wash the residue thoroughly. (Filtrate, reject.) Heat the residue with just 5 cc. of HCl and 10 cc. of water, and filter the boiling-hot solution if there is still a residue. Treat the solution by P. 21–22, 31–35, 51–57, and 71–77 to test for lead, bismuth, chromium, barium, strontium, and calcium.

In case the HCl left a residue, treat a fresh 1 g. sample of the substance by P. 2 and 3, and treat the residue so obtained by P. 7.

Notes. — 1. The boiling with Na_2CO_3 converts into carbonates the sulfates of lead, calcium, strontium, and bismuth completely, and at least 80 per cent of the sulfate of barium, even when large quantities of them are present. A second treatment, which should be applied to the residue if there are indications that barium is present, completely decomposes $BaSO_4$. The carbonates dissolve readily in hot HCl. Anhydrous chromic sulfate, which is left undissolved by dilute H_2SO_4 (P. 5) as a fine pink or gray powder, is slowly changed by boiling with Na_2CO_3 to a greenish blue hydroxide which dissolves in the HCl, leaving behind the still undecomposed sulfate. Antimonic oxide dissolves only to a small extent (2–4 mg.) in the Na_2CO_3 solution, but dissolves in the dilute HCl. Silver chloride is only slightly attacked by Na_3CO_2 solution.

2. Any residue insoluble in HCl can therefore consist only of barium or chromic sulfate, of silver chloride, or of some of the original substance still undecomposed, which is likely to consist of one of the native

oxides or silicates mentioned in Note 9, P. 5. If such a residue is obtained, it can ordinarily be rendered soluble by fusion with Na_2CO_3 and $NaNO_3$, as described in P. 7. It is, however, preferable to treat a fresh sample of the substance with HNO_3 and HCl (by P. 2 and 3), and to fuse the residue from that treatment with Na_2CO_3 and $NaNO_3$; for this makes it possible to detect in the aqueous extract of the fused mass certain acidic constituents, namely, fluoride, borate, and sulfate, which might otherwise escape detection.

Procedure 7. — *Fusion of the Residue with Sodium Carbonate.* — In case fusion with Na_2CO_3 is to be substituted for the HF treatment (P. 5), treat the residue undissolved by HNO_3 and HCl (P. 3 or 4) as described in the following paragraph. Or, in case HF has been used and HCl has left a residue in P. 6, and if a fresh sample of the substance has been treated by P. 2 and 3 (as directed in P. 6), treat the residue so obtained as described in the following paragraph.

Transfer the residue (see Note 2, P. 5) to a 30 cc. nickel crucible, mix it thoroughly with 10–20 cc. of anhydrous Na_2CO_3, cover the crucible, heat it strongly over a powerful burner, preferably within a cylinder of asbestos paper, so that complete fusion takes place, and continue the heating for 10–20 minutes. If dark particles of undecomposed substance can still be seen, add gradually in small portions 0.1–0.3 cc. of solid $NaNO_3$, and heat strongly for several minutes. Cool the crucible, place it in a casserole with 40–60 cc. of water, and boil the mixture till the fused mass is disintegrated. Filter, and wash the residue thoroughly.

Treat one half of the aqueous extract as directed in P. 123, to detect acidic constituents; and treat the other half as described in the next paragraph.

Rinse the residue not dissolved by water into a casserole with 15 cc. of 2 n. HNO_3, boil the mixture gently so long as the residue seems to be dissolving, and filter out and reject any undecomposed substance. Mix one tenth of this HNO_3 solution with one fifth of the half-portion of the aqueous extract, and acidify the mixture with HNO_3. If no precipitate forms, mix the rest of the HNO_3 solution with the remaining four-fifths of the half-portion of the aqueous extract, acidify the mixture, and treat it as described in the following paragraph. If a precipitate forms on mixing the HNO_3 solution and the aqueous extract, reject the mixed portions, and treat the remaining portions of the two solutions separately as described in the following paragraph, uniting the precipitates formed by the same group-reagent in the subsequent analysis.

Add 5 cc. of 12 n. HCl, and filter. Treat the precipitate by P. 12–13, to test for lead and silver. Evaporate the filtrate to dryness, and heat the residue till it becomes perfectly dry, by keeping the casserole in motion over a small flame. Add just 5 cc. of 6 n. HCl and 10 cc. of water, heat the mixture to boiling, and filter it. Wash the residue, and treat it by the first two paragraphs of P. 5, to confirm the presence of silica. Treat the filtrate by P. 21–79, to detect basic constituents.

Notes. — 1. Upon fusion with sodium carbonate most compounds undergo metathesis, the acidic constituent of the compound combining with the sodium and the basic element with the carbonate. The carbonate formed is, however, sometimes decomposed by heat with production of the oxide or of the metal itself. Acid-forming oxides, such as SiO_2, As_2O_5, and less rapidly Al_2O_3, expel CO_2 from the carbonate and form sodium salts. Such reactions are illustrated by the following equations:

$$BaSO_4 + Na_2CO_3 = Na_2SO_4 + BaCO_3.$$
$$Fe_2SiO_5 + Na_2CO_3 = Na_2SiO_3 + Fe_2O_3 + CO_2.$$
$$4\,AgCl + 2\,Na_2CO_3 = 4\,NaCl + 4\,Ag + 2\,CO_2 + O_2.$$
$$SiO_2 + Na_2CO_3 = Na_2SiO_3 + CO_2.$$

2. The $NaNO_3$ serves to oxidize some substances which are not much acted upon by Na_2CO_3 alone. Thus sulfides are converted into sulfates; chromium compounds, such as $Cr_2(SO_4)_3$ or $FeOCr_2O_3$ (the mineral chromite), into chromates; and manganese compounds into manganates.

3. After the treatment with water all the acidic constituents of the substance are found in the aqueous extract as sodium salts, and a portion of this extract is therefore reserved to be tested for these constituents. Certain of the basic constituents, namely arsenic, antimony, tin, aluminum, chromium, and manganese, may pass wholly or in part into the aqueous extract; and a part of this solution is therefore analyzed for basic constituents. Most of the basic constituents,

however, remain in the residue from the aqueous extract, and are dissolved by the dilute HNO₃.

4. To save time, the HNO₃ solution and the portion of the aqueous extract to be tested for basic constituents are mixed whenever this can be done without producing a precipitate. Whether a precipitate results is determined by the preliminary test with small portions of the solutions. The first and third equations in Note 1 are examples of cases in which the mixing would result in a precipitate.

5. HCl is added before the evaporation to precipitate silver and lead. A considerable quantity is added to destroy the nitrates, since the residue obtained by the subsequent evaporation is more soluble when in the state of chlorides.

6. The evaporation to dryness and subsequent heating at 100–130° serves to render silicic acid insoluble (see Note 6, P. 3).

7. A few substances, such as the native or ignited oxides of aluminum and tin, may be only partially attacked even by long-continued fusion with Na_2CO_3 and $NaNO_3$. Some silicates also may not be completely decomposed, especially if the substance was not very finely powdered; but enough of all of these substances is brought into solution to secure their detection. A residue from the HNO₃ treatment may therefore ordinarily be rejected.

8. A few milligrams of nickel are taken up from the crucible by the flux, so that this element, as well as the alkali elements, cannot be tested for later in the analysis. The crucible is, however, so little attacked by the flux that it can be used repeatedly.

9. Whenever it is permissible, it is somewhat better to make the fusion in a platinum crucible, since then no foreign substances are introduced from the crucible. It is not permissible, however, to ignite in platinum vessels compounds of the silver-, copper-, and tin-groups; for these may be reduced to the metal by heating with an alkaline flux. The same is true of sulfur, sulfides, and in the presence of organic matter of phosphates; for all these elements form easily fusible alloys with the platinum, and thus spoil the crucible. Moreover, alkaline hydroxides and strongly oxidizing fluxes (such as peroxides and nitrates) must not be fused in platinum, since they attack it fairly rapidly. Therefore, if the fusion is made in platinum, no more $NaNO_3$ should be added than is necessary.

Procedure 8. — *Treatment of Substances Containing Organic Matter.* — If the closed-tube test (P. 1) has shown the presence of organic matter, powder or cut into small pieces 1–5 g. of the substance (according to the quantity of organic matter present).

Add to it in a casserole about 10 cc. of 18 n. H_2SO_4; heat gradually until the substance is well charred; cool; add slowly, with constant stirring, under a hood, 16 n. HNO_3, until violent reaction ceases; warm gently for a few minutes, and then heat more strongly, keeping the dish moving, until the substance is thoroughly charred. Cool, again add 16 n. HNO_3 as before, and heat until thick fumes of H_2SO_4 are evolved. Repeat this process till the mixture becomes light-colored and remains so when heated strongly.

In case the substance has dissolved completely, evaporate the mixture carefully under a hood just to dryness, let the dish cool, and pour into it just 8 cc. of 6 n. H_2SO_4 and 10 cc. of water. If there is a residue, boil the mixture so long as it seems to be dissolving, filter out any residue still remaining, wash it, and treat it by P. 6. Treat the solution by P. 11.

In case the substance has not dissolved completely, transfer the mixture to a platinum or palladium-gold crucible, let it cool, and treat it (with HF) as described in the last three paragraphs of P. 5. (If the use of a platinum crucible or of HF is not practicable, treat the mixture as described in the foregoing paragraph, except that the residue undissolved by the dilute H_2SO_4 should be treated by P. 7, instead of by P. 6.)

Notes. — 1. This method of destroying organic matter is of very general application, being effective even when such stable substances as paraffin and cellulose are present. Organic matter can also be destroyed by ignition; but this has the disadvantages of volatilizing certain elements, especially mercury and arsenic, and of making some substances very difficultly soluble. When the organic matter consists only of oil, as is the case with an oil paint, it may advantageously be extracted with ether.

2. In case the substance dissolved completely in the concentrated H_2SO_4, it shows the absence of silica and silicates; for the silicic acid liberated by the decomposition of any silicate is dehydrated and made insoluble by heating with strong H_2SO_4. In this case the treatment with HF is omitted; and the solution is evaporated to remove the large quantity of H_2SO_4 so that it may not interfere with the H_2S precipitation, and the residue is treated with the proper quantity of dilute H_2SO_4. A small residue of sulfate of lead, barium, strontium,

or calcium, or of oxide of antimony, may then remain; and any such residue is treated by P. 6, to bring these elements in solution. If there is no such residue, it shows the absence of lead, barium, and strontium in the substance.

3. In case the substance did not dissolve completely in concentrated H_2SO_4, the mixture is treated with HF to detect and remove silica. There may still be a residue undissolved by the dilute H_2SO_4. This will contain any substances originally present that have not been attacked by HNO_3, H_2SO_4, or HF; all the lead, strontium, and barium that may have been present in any form, since the sulfates of these elements are very slightly soluble in dilute H_2SO_4; some of the calcium, bismuth, antimony, and tin, when these elements are present in considerable quantity, since their sulfates (or oxides) are not readily dissolved by dilute H_2SO_4; and substantially all of the chromium, since its sulfate is converted into the insoluble anhydrous form by heating with strong H_2SO_4.

Procedure 9. — *Treatment of Solutions.* — If the substance is a solution in water or other volatile solvent, test its effect upon litmus paper; and evaporate 10 cc. of it (after adding to it NH_4OH to alkaline reaction if it reddened litmus paper) in a small weighed dish to complete dryness over a steam-bath, so as not to overheat the residue; and weigh the dish again. Treat the residue or a portion of it by the first paragraph of P. 1 (heating it in a closed tube) to detect organic matter.

In case organic matter is proved absent, neutralize such a volume of the solution as contains 1 g. of solid substance exactly with HNO_3 or NH_4OH, bring the mixture to a volume of 10 cc. by evaporation or dilution, and add to it 5 cc. of 6 n. HNO_3. If no precipitate has separated from the solution, treat it by P. 11–89, to detect basic constituents. If a precipitate has separated, treat the mixture by P. 3 (and, if necessary, by P. 5–6 or 7), followed by P. 21–89, to detect basic constituents.

In case organic matter is found present, evaporate to dryness such a volume of the solution as contains 1 g. of solid substance, and treat the residue as directed in P. 8, to detect basic constituents.

In either case add to such a volume of the solution as contains 2.5 g. of solid substance 25 cc. of 3 n. Na_2CO_3 solution, evaporate the mixture to just 30 cc., filter it, and treat portions of the filtrate by P. 102–116, to detect acidic constituents.

Treat another portion of the solution, to detect carbonate and ammonium, as follows: Place 5–30 cc. of the solution in a distillation apparatus arranged as in P. 117, pour in through the safety-tube 5 cc. of HCl, distil off 2–3 cc. of liquid, and test the distillate for carbonate as in P. 117. Make the mixture in the flask alkaline with NaOH, distil off 5 cc. of the liquid into 5 cc. of water, and test the distillate for ammonium as in the second paragraph of P. 91.

Notes. — 1. A 10 cc. portion of the solution is evaporated to dryness and the residue is weighed, to determine how much dissolved substance is present and thus enable the usual amount of substance to be taken for analysis. NH$_4$OH is added when the solution is acid, to prevent the loss of volatile acids.

2. The solution, rather than the solid residue obtained from it, is tested for carbonate and for ammonium, since these constituents might be lost on evaporation.

DETECTION OF THE BASIC CONSTITUENTS

GENERAL DISCUSSION

THE science of qualitative chemical analysis treats of the methods of determining the nature of the elements and of the chemical compounds which are present in any given substance. When the presence or absence of the various elements is alone determined, the process is called ultimate analysis; when the chemical compounds of which the substance is composed are identified, it is called proximate analysis. In the analysis of inorganic substances, to which this book is devoted, the object in view is ordinarily an intermediate one — namely, that of detecting the base-forming and acid-forming constituents (called in this book simply the basic and acidic constituents) that are present in the substance. Thus the analysis of a substance consisting of calcium sulfate, zinc chromate, and ferric oxide would show not only that the elements calcium, sulfur, zinc, chromium, and iron were present, but also that the sulfur was in the form of sulfate (not sulfide or sulfite), the chromium in the form of chromate (not of a chromic salt), and the iron in the ferric (not the ferrous) state. The reason for this is that the analysis is carried out by dissolving the substance in water (with aid of acids, if necessary), and by treating the solution so obtained successively with a number of different chemical substances. Now, since the chemical reactions of substances in aqueous solutions are determined by the nature of the ions which they yield, and since the ions correspond to the basic and acidic constituents, it is these constituents whose presence or absence is established.

For detecting the basic constituents a systematic method is employed which consists in adding to an acid solution of the substance in succession ammonium chloride, hydrogen sulfide, ammonium hydroxide and sulfide, and ammonium carbonate.

By each of these reagents a group of basic constituents is precipitated. Thus, ammonium chloride precipitates those constituents whose chlorides are only slightly soluble in water; hydrogen sulfide, those whose sulfides are only slightly soluble in dilute acid; ammonium hydroxide and sulfide, those whose sulfides or hydroxides are only slightly soluble in ammoniacal solutions; and ammonium carbonate, those whose carbonates are only slightly soluble in water containing ammonium carbonate. The way in which the basic constituents are thus separated into groups is shown in more detail in Table II on the following page.

TABLE II. — SEPARATION OF THE BASIC CONSTITUENTS INTO GROUPS

Solution in Dilute Nitric Acid Containing All the Common Basic Constituents.   *Add NH_4Cl (P. 11).*

Precipitate: SILVER-GROUP (Pb, Ag, Hg), as chlorides.* See Table III.

Filtrate. *Saturate with H_2S gas (P. 21).*

   Precipitate: COPPER-GROUP and TIN-GROUP as sulfides. *Treat with Na_2S–Na_2S_2 solution.* See Table IV.

      Solution: TIN-GROUP (Hg, As, Sb, Sn), as sodium sulfo-salts. See Table VI.

      Residue: COPPER-GROUP (Pb, Bi, Cu, Cd), as sulfides. See Table V.

   Filtrate: *Add NH_4OH and $(NH_4)_2S$ (P. 51).*

      Precipitate: ALUMINUM-GROUP and IRON-GROUP, as hydroxides and sulfides. *Dissolve in acid, add $NaOH$ and Na_2O_2 (P. 52).* See Table VII.

         Filtrate: ALUMINUM-GROUP (Al, Zn, Cr), as sodium salts. See Table VIII.

         Precipitate: IRON-GROUP (Mn, Fe, Co, Ni), as hydroxides. See Tables IX and X.

      Filtrate: *Add $(NH_4)_2CO_3$ (P. 71).*

         Precipitate: ALKALINE-EARTH GROUP (Ba, Sr, Ca, Mg), as carbonates. See Table XI.

         Filtrate: ALKALI-GROUP (NH₄, K, Na), as nitrates and chlorides. See Tables XII and XIII.

---

* Lead is precipitated with the silver-group only when a large quantity is present, and then only partially; mercury is precipitated only when it is in the mercurous state.

PRECIPITATION AND ANALYSIS OF THE SILVER-GROUP

TABLE III. — ANALYSIS OF THE SILVER-GROUP.

Precipitate: $PbCl_2$, $AgCl$, Hg_2Cl_2.   *Treat with hot water (P. 12).*

Solution: $PbCl_2$. *Add K_2CrO_4 (P. 12).*	Residue: $AgCl$, Hg_2Cl_2. *Pour NH_4OH through the filter (P. 13).*	
Precipitate: $PbCrO_4$	Black residue: Hg and $Hg\genfrac{}{}{0pt}{}{Cl}{NH_2}$.	Solution: $Ag(NH_3)_2Cl$. *Add HNO_3 (P. 13).*
		Precipitate: $AgCl$.

Procedure 11. — *Precipitation of the Silver-Group.* — Pour the cold solution of the substance (prepared by P. 2 or by P. 5–9, and containing 30 milliequivalents of HNO_3 or about 50 milliequivalents of H_2SO_4 in about 15 cc. of solution) into a conical flask (see Note 1), and add to it 4 cc. of 3 n. NH_4Cl solution (see Notes 2 and 3). (White precipitate, presence of SILVER-GROUP.) Let the mixture stand for 3 or 4 minutes; then filter it. Wash the precipitate with 5–10 cc. of cold 2 n. HCl, rejecting the washings. (Precipitate, P. 12; filtrate, P. 21.)

Notes. — 1. *It is recommended that in general hard-glass conical flasks (the so-called Erlenmeyer flasks of hard glass), rather than beakers or test-tubes, be employed for holding solutions that are being subjected to the operations of precipitation and heating.*

2. Even in cases where it is not essential to add a perfectly definite volume of a reagent, the analyst should make it a practice to measure out the quantity to be added, rather than to pour in an indefinite quantity from the reagent bottle. For this purpose a 10 cc. graduate should be constantly at hand. For adding smaller quantities than 2 cc. a dropper should be used. This may be made by drawing out one end of a short glass tube to a wide capillary and capping the other end with a rubber nipple. When more of a reagent than is needed has been poured into a graduate or other vessel, it should never be poured back into the reagent bottle, owing to the danger of contaminating the reagent.

3. *Unless the concentration is specified, as is done in this case, it is understood that all salt solutions used as reagents are 1 normal (1 n.), that is, that they contain one equivalent of salt per liter of solution; also that, unless otherwise specified, the acid and base solutions used as reagents are 6 normal (6 n.).*

4. By one *equivalent* of any substance is meant that weight of it which reacts with one atomic weight (1.008 grams) of hydrogen in any of its compounds or with the weight of any other substance which itself reacts with one atomic weight of hydrogen. Thus, one equivalent is the quantity in grams corresponding to the following formulas: 1 NaOH, $\frac{1}{2}$ Ba(OH)$_2$, 1 HCl, $\frac{1}{2}$ H$_2$SO$_4$, $\frac{1}{3}$ H$_3$PO$_4$, 1 NH$_4$Cl, $\frac{1}{2}$ Na$_2$SO$_4$, $\frac{1}{2}$ CaSO$_4$, $\frac{1}{3}$ FeCl$_3$. The equivalent weight of a substance is evidently not identical with its *molecular weight*, which is ordinarily the number of grams represented by its formula; thus one equivalent of H$_2$SO$_4$ is 49.04 grams, but one molecular weight is 98.08 grams. When a substance may take part either in a reaction of metathesis or in one of oxidation and reduction, its *metathetical equivalent* has to be distinguished from its *oxidation equivalent*. Thus, the metathetical equivalent of nitric acid is 1 HNO$_3$; but its oxidation equivalent (when it is reduced to NO) is $\frac{1}{3}$ HNO$_3$. In this book the term *equivalent* will always be used to denote the metathetical equivalent. Note that the number of equivalents of a substance is a certain quantity of it; but that the terms *normal* and *molal* denote its *concentration*, that is, the quantity of it per unit-volume; normal signifying the number of equivalents of it per liter, and molal, the number of molecular weights per liter.

5. If NH$_4$Cl produces no precipitate, it proves the absence of silver and mercurous mercury, but not of lead, since PbCl$_2$ is fairly soluble in water even in the presence of chlorides. Thus, under the conditions of this Procedure not more than 50 mg. of lead remain in solution.

6. The solubility of PbCl$_2$ is much smaller in a solution of NH$_4$Cl or of any other chloride than it is in water, owing to the so-called common-ion effect, which may be explained in detail as follows: The mass-action law requires that at a given temperature in all dilute solutions containing lead chloride the ratio of the product of the ion-concentrations* (Pb^{++})$\times$(Cl$^-$)^2 to the concentration (PbCl$_2$) of the unionized salt have the same value; that is, (Pb^{++})$\times$(Cl$^-$)$^2\div$(PbCl$_2$) = some definite value. Now in all solutions which have been saturated with lead chloride as a result of sufficiently long contact with the solid substance, the concentration of the lead chloride present as such (that is, as unionized PbCl$_2$) must evidently have the same value, and there-

---

* In mass-action expressions of this kind, chemical formulas within parentheses denote the *concentrations* of the respective substances, that is, the quantities of them per liter of solution.

fore in all such saturated solutions the ion-concentration product $(Pb^{++}) \times (Cl^-)^2$ must also have the same value; that is, in all solutions saturated at a given temperature with lead chloride, $(Pb^{++}) \times (Cl^-)^2 =$ some definite value. This particular value which the ion-concentration product has when the solution is saturated is commonly called the *solubility-product;* but the principles involved are less likely to be misunderstood if it be called the *saturation-value of the ion-concentration product.* The saturation-value varies, of course, with the nature of the salt, and with the temperature in the case of a given salt. In the case of lead chloride at 20°, whose solubility in water at 20° will be seen by reference to the Table of Solubilities in the Appendix to be 70 milliequivalents per liter, the saturation-value of the ion-concentration product in millimols per liter is evidently $(35) \times (70)^2 = 171,500$, provided the ionization be considered to be complete, as may be assumed to be true in these qualitative considerations in the case of nearly all neutral salts. Any solution containing lead-ion and chloride-ion in which the ion-concentration product exceeds this saturation-value is evidently supersaturated and tends to deposit the solid substance; and any solution in which the ion-concentration product is less than the saturation-value is evidently undersaturated and tends to dissolve more of the solid substance. Now, when NH_4Cl or HCl is added to a saturated solution of $PbCl_2$ in water, the immediate effect is to increase the value of (Cl^-), and therefore of the product $(Pb^{++}) \times (Cl^-)^2$; but the solution becomes thereby supersaturated, and $PbCl_2$ will precipitate out of it until the saturation-value of the product $(Pb^{++}) \times (Cl^-)^2$ is restored.

7. Bismuth and antimony might be precipitated by the NH_4Cl as oxychlorides ($BiOCl$ and $SbOCl$), if the directions for preparing the solution of the original substance were not followed. But under the prescribed procedure, which yields a mixture with a fairly large acid concentration, these elements remain in solution; for their oxychlorides, though only very slightly soluble in water, dissolve readily in sufficiently concentrated acid.

8. The precipitate is washed with 2 n. HCl, rather than with water, first, in order that bismuth and antimony may not be precipitated as oxychlorides in the filter, and secondly, in order that as little $PbCl_2$ as possible be dissolved. Only a small volume (5–10 cc.) is used, so as not to dissolve much $PbCl_2$. Stronger HCl is not used, since it would dissolve more $PbCl_2$, $AgCl$, and Hg_2Cl_2, owing to the formation of acids with complex anions, such as $H^+_2PbCl_4^=$, $H^+_2AgCl_3^=$, and $H^+_2HgCl_4^=$. The acid washings are not added to the filtrate, so that the acid concentration may be properly adjusted in the subsequent H_2S precipitation.

Procedure 12. — *Extraction and Detection of Lead.* — Pour repeatedly through the filter containing the NH_4Cl precipitate (P. 11) a 10 cc. portion of boiling water (see Note 1). Wash the residue thoroughly with hot water, and treat it by P. 13. Cool the 10 cc. portion of water, and add to it 2 cc. of HNO_3 and 2 cc. of 3 n. K_2CrO_4 solution (see Notes 2 and 3, P. 11). (Yellow precipitate, presence of LEAD.)

Notes. — 1. *When it is directed to dissolve a precipitate by pouring the solvent repeatedly through the filter, this is best done by pouring a single portion of the solvent from one test-tube through the filter into another test-tube, back and forth, three or four times. When the solvent is to be used hot (as in this Procedure), it should be heated to boiling between each pouring.*

2. Owing to the imperfect washing of the NH_4Cl precipitate, the aqueous extract may contain, besides lead, small quantities of other elements. Barium, if present, would give a precipitate with the K_2CrO_4 in neutral solution; but this is prevented by the addition of the 2 cc. of HNO_3. The use of much more HNO_3 or of much less K_2CrO_4 solution would so increase the solubility of $PbCrO_4$ as to seriously diminish the delicacy of the lead test.

Procedure 13. — *Detection of Silver and Mercury.* — Pour repeatedly through the filter containing the residue insoluble in hot water (P. 12) a 5–10 cc. portion of NH_4OH (see Note 1). (Black residue on the filter, presence of MERCUROUS MERCURY.) Acidify the filtrate with HNO_3. (White precipitate, presence of SILVER.) When there is much black residue and little or no white precipitate, treat the residue by P. 14.

Notes. — 1. *When two quite different limiting quantities of the reagent are specified (for example, 5–10 cc. as in this Procedure), the quantity added should be adjusted to the size of the precipitate. The upper limit is so specified as to provide for the presence of 500 mg. of the element concerned.*

2. The black residue that is produced by the action of NH_4OH on Hg_2Cl_2 is a mixture of finely divided mercury with the white mercuric compound $HgClNH_2$. The reaction is expressed by the equation:

$$\underline{Hg_2Cl_2} + 2\ NH_4OH = \underline{HgClNH_2} + \underline{Hg} + NH_4^+Cl^- + 2\ H_2O.$$

The compound $HgClNH_2$ may be considered to be a derivative of

$HgCl_2$, formed by replacing an atom of chlorine by the univalent radical NH_2.

3. An NH_4OH solution contains a considerable proportion of (un-hydrated) NH_3; and $AgCl$ dissolves readily in it, owing to the formation of a soluble complex salt, $Ag(NH_3)_2Cl$, which in solution is largely ionized into $Ag(NH_3)_2^+$ and Cl^- ions. This complex cation has so slight a tendency to dissociate into Ag^+ and NH_3 that the ratio of its concentration to that of the simple Ag^+ ion is about 10^7 in a normal solution of NH_4OH.

4. If the $PbCl_2$ was not completely extracted from the NH_4Cl precipitate by boiling water (in P. 12), it is converted into a basic salt $(Pb(OH)Cl)$ by the NH_4OH, and may pass through the filter, yielding a turbid filtrate. This basic salt will, however, dissolve on the addition of HNO_3.

Procedure 14. — *Detection of Silver in the Presence of Much Mercury.* — Wash the black residue undissolved by NH_4OH (P. 13), and pour repeatedly through the filter containing it a mixture of 3 cc. of HCl and 10 cc. of saturated Br_2 solution, at the same time rubbing the residue with a glass rod. Wash the filter, and pour repeatedly through it a 10 cc. portion of NH_4OH. Acidify the solution with HNO_3. (Yellowish-white precipitate, presence of SILVER.)

Notes. — 1. When much mercury is present a considerable quantity of silver (5 mg. or more) may be so completely retained in the black residue that scarcely any test for silver is obtained in P. 13. This is probably due to the fact that the AgCl is reduced to metallic silver by the metallic mercury. When much mercury is present it is therefore necessary to test the residue for silver, as described in this Procedure.

2. The Br_2 converts the mercury in the residue into soluble $HgBr_2$, and the silver into insoluble AgBr. The HCl dissolves the $HgClNH_2$ present in the residue with formation of $HgCl_2$.

PRECIPITATION AND SEPARATION OF THE COPPER AND TIN GROUPS

TABLE IV. — PRECIPITATION AND SEPARATION OF THE COPPER AND TIN GROUPS.

Hydrogen Sulfide Precipitate:
PbS, Bi_2S_3, CuS, CdS.
HgS, As_2S_3, As_2S_5, Sb_2S_3, Sb_2S_5, SnS, SnS_2.
Treat with Na_2S–Na_2S_2 solution (P. 22).

Residue: PbS, Bi_2S_3, CuS, CdS. See Table V.	Solution: Na_2HgS_2, Na_3AsS_4, Na_3SbS_4, Na_2SnS_3. *Acidify with HCl (P. 23).*	
	Precipitate: HgS, As_2S_5, Sb_2S_5, SnS_2, S. See Table VI.	Filtrate: NaCl. *Reject.*

Procedure 21. — *Precipitation of the Copper and Tin Groups.* — Dilute to 100 cc. the filtrate from the NH_4Cl precipitate (P. 11) or the solution of the substance in HCl or H_2SO_4 (P. 3–9), which should contain about 30 milliequivalents of HNO_3 or HCl, or 50 milliequivalents of H_2SO_4. Pour this solution, without filtering off any precipitate, into a conical flask provided with a two-hole rubber stopper in which is a tube leading to the bottom of the flask. Pass into the cold solution through a gas wash-bottle a slow current of H_2S, till, upon closing the hole in the stopper and shaking the flask, the gas no longer continues to bubble through the wash-bottle into the solution. Filter, wash the precipitate with hot water (see Note 1), and treat it by P. 22, after uniting with it any further precipitate obtained by the H_2S treatment described in the last paragraph of this Procedure. Heat the filtrate nearly to boiling (to 70–90°), and pass H_2S into it at that temperature for 5–10 minutes.

In case there is no further precipitate, treat 5 cc. of the solution by P. 50 and the remainder by P. 51.

In case there is a further precipitate, add 5 cc. of 12 n. HCl, and evaporate the mixture just to dryness (see Note 2). Then add 10 cc. of 6 n. HCl_1 saturate the cold solution with H_2S, heat it to 70–90°, and pass H_2S into it for 5–10 minutes. Cool the mixture, dilute it to 100 cc., and saturate it with H_2S. Filter out the precipitate, wash it, and unite it with the first H_2S precipitate. Treat 5 cc. of the filtrate by P. 50 and the remainder by P. 51.

Notes. — 1. *The washing of precipitates should in general be continued until the wash-water will no longer give a test for any substance known to be present in the filtrate (for example, in this case for acid with blue litmus-paper or for chloride with $AgNO_3$). Precipitates which are practically insoluble in water (like all the sulfides and hydroxides that are met with in this system of analysis) are best washed with nearly boiling water, as this runs through the filter more rapidly and extracts soluble substances more readily. Precipitates which are appreciably soluble should be washed with cold water and with only a small quantity of it. The proper method of washing a precipitate is to cause a fine stream of water from a wash-bottle to play upon the upper edge of the filter (and in larger quantity on the three-fold part of it). The wash-water should in general not be allowed to run into the filtrate, so as not to dilute it unnecessarily. When, however, a considerable proportion of the solution would be retained in the filter and precipitate, it is well to add the first washings to the filtrate.*

2. *When it is directed to evaporate a solution almost to dryness or just to dryness, the last part of the evaporation should be carried out by keeping the dish moving over a small flame in such a way as not to overheat the residue and as to avoid bumping. The expression " almost to dryness " implies that the evaporation is discontinued while the residue is still moist (with 0.5–1.0 cc. of the solution); the expression " just to dryness," that it is continued till the residue becomes dry (but without any of it having been heated above about 125°).*

3. The H^+ ion concentration has been made 0.3 normal (by diluting 5 cc. of 6 n. HNO_3 or HCl to 100 cc.) and the solution is saturated with H_2S gas in the cold, since under these conditions there is a precipitate with even 1 mg. of cadmium, lead, or tin (the elements of the copper- and tin-groups least readily precipitated), and there remain in solution even 300 mg. of zinc (the element of the aluminum- and iron-groups most likely to precipitate). (This statement in regard to zinc is true, however, only when the solution contains also a considerable quantity of chloride-ion, such as was added in P. 11, and when it is not allowed to stand.) Moreover, even when a small quantity of any of the elements of the aluminum- and iron-groups is present with a large quantity of a copper-group element, the former is not carried down in the

H_2S precipitate under these conditions to such an extent as to prevent its detection in the filtrate, provided as much of it as 1 mg., or in some combinations as much as 2 mg., is present.

4. The formation of a white precipitate on diluting the solution to 100 cc. shows the presence of considerable bismuth or antimony. The precipitate, which consists of BiOCl or SbOCl, need not be filtered off, as these substances are converted into sulfides by H_2S. The formation, on passing in H_2S, of a white or yellowish precipitate which rapidly turns black with more H_2S indicates mercury. (The white compound is $HgCl_2 \cdot 2\,HgS$, and this is converted into black HgS by the excess of H_2S.) The formation of an orange precipitate shows antimony; of a yellow one, cadmium, arsenic, or stannic tin. All the other sulfides are black or brownish black.

5. The precipitation of bismuth and antimony on diluting the filtrate from the silver-group arises from the fact that their normal salts ($BiCl_3$, $Bi(NO_3)_3$, $SbCl_3$, etc.), though very soluble in fairly concentrated acids, are hydrolyzed (decomposed by water) with formation of oxysalts ($BiOCl$, $BiONO_3$, $SbOCl$, etc.) which are only slightly soluble in water. Equilibrium is established between the precipitate and the solution in accordance with the mass-action law, which requires that the concentration of bismuth or antimony in the solution increase rapidly with the concentration of the acid. Under the conditions of this Procedure bismuth precipitates when more than 50 mg. are present, and antimony when more than 15 mg. are present.

6. The effect of acid on the precipitation of the sulfides is explained by the mass-action law and ionic theory as follows: When a dilute solution, whether aqueous or acid, is saturated at a definite temperature with H_2S gas under the atmospheric (or any definite) pressure, the H_2S present as such in the solution always has the same concentration. This ionizes, however, to a slight extent into H^+ and HS^-, and to a still less extent into $2\,H^+$ and $S^=$. It is only the latter form of ionization that needs to be considered here. Now between the H_2S and its ions must be maintained the equilibrium expressed by the equation $(H^+)^2 \times (S^=) = const. \times (H_2S)$; or, since in this case $(H_2S) = const.$, as just stated, it follows that also $(H^+)^2 \times (S^=) = const.$ From this it is evident that when (H^+) is increased by the addition of acid to the solution, $(S^=)$ must be decreased in the proportion in which the square of (H^+) is increased; thus, if (H^+) is doubled, $(S^=)$ will be reduced to one-fourth. But in order that a sulfide — for example, of the formula $M^{++}S^=$ — may precipitate, the concentration-product $(M^{++}) \times (S^=)$ must attain its saturation-value. This value varies, however, with the nature of the sulfide and with the temperature; and therefore the acid concentration that will barely permit of precipitation when (M^{++})

has a definite value (for example, 1 mg. in 100 cc.) will be different for different sulfides and for the same sulfide at different temperatures. Thus, if the elements are arranged in the order in which they are precipitated from cold HCl solutions as the acid-concentration is progressively decreased, the series is approximately as follows: arsenic, mercury and copper, antimony, bismuth and stannic tin, cadmium, lead and stannous tin, zinc, cobalt, nickel, iron, manganese. The acid concentration which permits precipitation also varies with the ionization of the acid; thus zinc is precipitated from a fairly concentrated solution of acetic acid, since, owing to the slight ionization of this acid, the H^+ concentration is less than in a far more dilute solution of HCl. The three acids, HCl, HNO_3, and H_2SO_4, afford another instance of the effect of difference in ionization. As will be seen from the Table of Ionization Values in the Appendix, the first two of these acids are almost completely ionized at moderate concentrations; but, in the case of H_2SO_4, while the first hydrogen is almost completely dissociated, the second hydrogen is split off (from the ion HSO_4^-) to only a moderate extent (about 25%), so that in order to yield a hydrogen-ion concentration of 0.3 normal, about 50 milliequivalents of H_2SO_4 have to be present in 100 cc. of solution (instead of the 30 milliequivalents of HCl or HNO_3).

7. The solution is filtered, heated nearly to boiling, and again saturated with H_2S, in order to insure the detection of arsenic; for this element, when present in the higher state of oxidation (as arsenic acid) is only very slowly precipitated by H_2S in the cold. At 70–90° the precipitation is much more rapid, especially if the solution has been previously saturated with H_2S in the cold. Under these conditions even 1 mg. of arsenic gives a distinct precipitate in less than 5 minutes. Continuous treatment with H_2S at 70–90° in an open vessel does not, however, completely precipitate a large quantity of arsenic from such a weakly acid solution even within an hour. For this reason, when a considerable precipitate forms in the hot solution, it is directed to evaporate the filtrate, to add HCl to destroy the HNO_3 (which in the concentrated state would decompose the H_2S), to dissolve the residue in HCl, and to pass H_2S through the hot solution. From this concentrated acid solution the arsenic precipitates completely in 5–10 minutes. The reasons for this peculiar behavior of arsenic in the higher state of oxidation are stated in the following note. The solution is finally diluted and saturated in the cold with H_2S, since the other elements are not completely precipitated until the arsenic has been removed.

8. When a solution of H_3AsO_4 in dilute HCl is treated with H_2S, soluble sulfarsenic acid (H_3AsO_3S) is formed, which explains why the solution may absorb much of the gas before a precipitate appears.

This compound is decomposed slowly in the cold, but much more rapidly on heating, with precipitation of a sulfide of arsenic (As_2S_3 and S_2 when excess of H_2S is not present; As_2S_5 when the solution is kept saturated with the gas). This decomposition takes place more rapidly, the greater the concentration of the acid. In fairly concentrated HCl solution H_3AsO_4 is also directly converted by excess of H_2S into As_2S_5. The slow precipitation of arsenic when in the form of H_3AsO_4 (or H_3AsO_3S) is due to the extremely small concentration of arsenic-ion (As^{+++++}) in the solution; and the fact that its precipitation, unlike that of the other elements, is greatly promoted by a large HCl concentration doubtless arises from a partial conversion of the H_3AsO_4 into $AsCl_5$, which by its ionization yields arsenic-ion.

9. A white, finely divided precipitate of free sulfur will be formed if the solution contains substances capable of oxidizing H_2S. The most important of these likely to be present are ferric salts, chromates, permanganates, and chlorates. In dilute solution the reduction by H_2S of ferric salts to ferrous is attended by a change in color from yellow to colorless; of chromates to chromic salts, from orange to green; and of permanganates to manganous salts, from purple to colorless. Nitric acid, if it were fairly concentrated, would also destroy the H_2S; but at the concentration in question (0.3 normal) it has scarcely any oxidizing action even in boiling solution.

10. In balancing equations expressing reactions of oxidation and reduction, like those referred to in the preceding note, the main thing is to determine the number of molecules of the oxidizing and reducing substances which react with one another. This can be done most simply by considering, in the way illustrated by the following examples, the changes which take place in the valences of the atoms of these substances. Thus, in the reduction of a ferric to a ferrous salt by hydrogen sulfide, the iron atom changes in valence from $+3$ to $+2$, and the sulfur atom changes in valence from -2 (in H_2S) to zero (in ordinary sulfur). Since the total change in the number of valences must be equal and opposite in the two substances, it is evident that two molecules of ferric salt react with one of hydrogen sulfide, and therefore that the equation is:

$$2\ FeCl_3 + H_2S = 2\ FeCl_2 + \underline{S} + 2\ HCl.$$

In the reduction of $HClO_3$ to HCl by H_2S, the chlorine atom decreases in valence from $+5$ to -1 (thus by six positive valences); hence there must be a decrease of six negative valences in the reducing substance, and that this may be the case three molecules of H_2S are evidently required. The equation is therefore:

$$HClO_3 + 3\ H_2S = HCl + 3\ \underline{S} + 3\ H_2O.$$

In cases where the valence of an atom in a substance is in doubt, it can be found at once from the valences of the other atoms with the aid of the principle that in any compound the sum of all the positive valences is equal to the sum of all the negative valences; thus in chloric acid $HClO_3$, since the three oxygen atoms have 6 negative valences and the hydrogen atom has 1 positive valence, the chlorine atom must, in order to make the compound neutral, have 5 positive valences.

Consider as another example the reduction of potassium permanganate ($KMnO_4$) to manganous chloride ($MnCl_2$) by H_2S in the presence of HCl. The number of valences of the manganese atom is seen to be $+7$ in $KMnO_4$ (since that of four oxygen atoms is -8 and that of the potassium atom is $+1$) and to be $+2$ in $MnCl_2$. The proportion is therefore $2\ KMnO_4 : 5\ H_2S$, and the reaction is:

$$2\ KMnO_4 + 5\ H_2S + 6\ HCl = 2\ MnCl_2 + 2\ KCl + 5\ \underline{S} + 8\ H_2O.$$

The amount of acid required in such cases can be seen by inspection, — most readily by noting how many hydrogen atoms are needed to combine with the oxygen atoms of the substance undergoing reduction. Thus in this case 16 hydrogen atoms are evidently needed for this purpose; and, since 10 are furnished by the H_2S, 6 more must be supplied by adding 6 molecules of HCl (or an equivalent quantity of some other acid).

Procedure 22. — *Separation of the Copper-Group from the Tin-Group by Sodium Sulfide.* — Transfer the H_2S precipitate (P. 21) to a casserole (see Note 1), and add to it 3–10 cc. (see Note 2, P. 11, and Note 1, P. 13) of Na_2S reagent. Cover the dish, and heat the mixture to 50–70° for 3–5 minutes with constant agitation. Add 5–10 cc. of water, and filter. (Residue, presence of the COPPER-GROUP.) Wash the residue thoroughly with hot water. (See Note 1, P. 21.) (Residue, P. 31; solution, P. 23.)

Notes.—1. *When a precipitate is to be transferred to a casserole, the filter is opened, the portions to which no precipitate adheres are torn off, and the remainder is laid along the side of a casserole; the solvent is then poured over it and is swashed to and fro, the precipitate being rubbed at the same time with a glass rod, so as to remove it from the filter. If this succeeds, the filter is drawn out of the solution, the liquid pressed out of it with a glass rod, and the paper thrown away; otherwise the filter is allowed to disintegrate and is filtered out together with any residue.*

2. The Na_2S reagent is a solution 3 normal in Na_2S, 1 normal in Na_2S_2, and 1 normal in $NaOH$. It is prepared by dissolving sulfur in a solution of Na_2S and $NaOH$. The $NaOH$ serves to diminish the hydrolysis of the sulfides.

3. Sodium sulfide dissolves the sulfides of the tin-group because it converts them into soluble salts of sulfo-acids with complex anions. In the case of the higher sulfides the reactions are as follows:

$$As_2S_5 + 3\ Na^+{}_2S^= = 2\ Na^+{}_3\ AsS_4^{---}.$$
$$\overline{Sb_2S_5} + 3\ Na^+{}_2S^= = 2\ Na^+{}_3\ SbS_4^{---}.$$
$$\overline{SnS_2} + Na^+{}_2S^= = Na^+{}_2\ SnS_3^=.$$
$$\overline{HgS} + Na^+{}_2S^= = Na^+{}_2\ HgS_2^=.$$

The excess of sulfur present in the form of Na_2S_2 in the reagent oxidizes the lower sulfides (As_2S_3, Sb_2S_3, SnS) to the same sulfosalts as are produced by the action of Na_2S on the higher sulfides. It will be seen that these sulfosalts are analogous to the salts of the familiar oxygen acids of these elements, the difference being that sulfur has replaced oxygen; and they are so named as to indicate this relationship. Thus the four sulfosalts whose formulas are given above are called sodium sulfarsenate, sulfantimonate, sulfostannate, and sulfomercurate.

4. For separating the copper-group from the tin-group a sulfide reagent containing no Na_2S_2 may be used in case any tin present must be in the higher state of oxidation as a result of the use of concentrated HNO_3 (in P. 3 or 4) in preparing the solution of the original substance. This has, however, no decided advantages; and it has the defect that the separation of a small quantity of mercury from a large quantity of copper or cadmium is less complete. The reagent containing Na_2S_2 must be used in case tin may be present in the lower state of oxidation; for sodium monosulfide does not dissolve SnS.

5. The behavior of the various sulfides when warmed with 10 cc. of the Na_2S reagent is as follows: Of the sulfides of the copper-group, only a little bismuth and a little copper (up to 1 mg. of each) dissolve. Of the sulfides of the tin-group, more than 500 mg. of any of them pass into solution. Even when a large quantity (500 mg.) of any one basic constituent is present, the separation is sharp enough to enable a small quantity (1–2 mg.) of any other basic constituent to be detected in the subsequent analysis; except that a little mercury (up to 2 mg.) may remain almost entirely in the copper-group residue when a large quantity (500 mg.) of copper or cadmium is present.

6. Ammonium monosulfide and disulfide are employed in most schemes of qualitative analysis for the separation of the sulfides precipitated by H_2S into two groups; but the sodium sulfide reagent here utilized has the following advantages. The quantity of copper dis-

solved by the Na₂S reagent (1 mg. in 10 cc.) is much less than that (5–10 mg.) dissolved by the ammonium disulfide reagent. The Na₂S reagent dissolves mercury, thus separating it from the copper-group; while the ammonium sulfide reagents leave it undissolved in the copper-group residue, with the disadvantage that the precipitate of mercuric sulfide may retain considerable cadmium (up to 5 mg.), making its detection less delicate. Moreover, in the sodium sulfide separation the presence of tin causes no complications; but in the ammonium sulfide process, in case a small quantity (2–15 mg.) of tin is present with a large quantity (100–500 mg.) of any element of the copper-group, all the tin may remain in the undissolved residue, making it necessary to provide for its detection at two places in the scheme of analysis. Finally, the sodium sulfide reagent is prepared more easily and in a more standard condition. On the other hand, the Na₂S reagent has the disadvantages that it dissolves a little bismuth (1 mg. in 10 cc.), while the ammonium sulfide reagents leave it entirely undissolved, and that it fails to separate a small quantity of mercury (up to 2 mg.) from a large quantity of copper or cadmium.

Procedure 23. — *Precipitation of the Tin-Group.* — To the Na₂S solution (P. 22) in a small flask gradually add HCl till the mixture becomes acid (see Note 1), then add 1 cc. more, and shake the mixture for a minute or two.

In case the precipitate is nearly white (see Note 5) (showing the absence of the TIN-GROUP), reject the mixture.

In case the precipitate is black, yellow, or orange colored (showing the presence of the TIN-GROUP), filter it out and wash it with the aid of suction (see Note 2), finally sucking it as dry as possible. Reject the filtrate, and treat the precipitate immediately by P. 41. *– Add a H₄Cl crystals – heat to 98° F*

In case the precipitate is neither nearly white nor of a pronounced black, yellow, or orange color (making doubtful the presence or absence of the TIN-GROUP), transfer it to a casserole, warm it with 8 cc. of NH₄OH for 2–3 minutes with frequent agitation, and filter. Treat the residue, if it is dark colored (showing the possible presence of MERCURY), by P. 42–43. To the filtrate add 5 drops of (NH₄)₂S reagent, heat it to boiling, filter out any precipitate, add to the solution 10 cc. of water, acidify the mixture with HCl (see Note 1), and shake it for a minute or two. If the precipitate is yellow or orange colored (showing the presence of ARSENIC, ANTIMONY, or TIN), filter it out, wash it, and treat it by P. 41–47 (omitting P. 42 for the separation of mercury). If the precipitate is white (showing the absence of ARSENIC, ANTIMONY, and TIN), reject it.

Notes. — 1. *Whenever it is directed to make a solution acid or alkaline, this should be done carefully as follows : Add from a graduate somewhat less acid or alkali than will neutralize the alkali or acid known to be present in the solution. Then add from a dropper more of the acid or alkali,* 10–15 *drops at a time, till a glass rod dipped in the solution and touched to a piece of blue or red litmus paper placed on a watch-glass changes the color of the litmus to a pronounced red or blue (not to an intermediate purple color).* Thus in this case, if 10 cc. of 5 n. Na_2S reagent were used and none was lost in the operations, 8.3 cc. of 6 n. HCl would be needed to neutralize it, and 6–7 cc. of it might be rapidly added, after which the remainder would be added slowly from a dropper till a drop of the mixture gave a pure red color to litmus paper.

2. *In cases where the precipitate is voluminous, where the precipitate must be washed with very little water, or where (as in this case) it must be freed as far as possible from water, it is advisable to filter with the aid of suction. This operation is carried out by reinforcing the ordinary filter with a small hardened filter placed below it in the funnel, inserting the funnel in a rubber stopper in the neck of a filter-bottle, and connecting the side-arm of the filter-bottle to a suction-pump by means of a rubber tube carrying a screw-clamp. The suction should be applied very gradually so as to avoid breaking the filter. The filtrate should be poured out of the filter-bottle before beginning to wash the precipitate.*

3. When the HCl is added to the solution of the sulfosalts, the corresponding sulfoacids which are liberated decompose immediately into H_2S and the solid sulfides. These are now necessarily in the higher state of oxidation, since the lower sulfides, if originally present, have been oxidized by the Na_2S_2 present in the Na_2S reagent. The fact that the sulfide precipitates when the solution of the sulfosalt is acidified is a consequence of the mass-action law. Thus, the complex anions dissociate according to the equations,

$$\underline{SnS_3^=} = SnS_2 + S^=, \quad 2\,AsS_4^{---} = \underline{As_2S_5} + 3\,S^=,$$
$$2\,SbS_4^{---} = \underline{Sb_2S_5} + 3\,S^=;$$

and the mass-action law evidently requires that, in any solution saturated with the solid sulfide, the concentration of the complex anion, and therefore of the tin, arsenic, or antimony in the solution, increase with increasing concentration of the $S^=$ ion. Now in the solution of the largely ionized Na_2S there is a large concentration of $S^=$ ion; but when the solution is made acid with HCl, the $S^=$ ion is almost completely converted by the relatively large concentration of the H^+ ion into the slightly ionized substances HS^- and H_2S.

4. The sulfide solution must be made distinctly acid in order to insure decomposition of the sulfosalts; but a large excess of acid must be avoided lest SnS_2 redissolve.

5. When the Na_2S reagent itself is acidified, a considerable pale-yellow or grayish-white precipitate of sulfur results, in consequence of the decomposition of the Na_2S_2 in the reagent. This may make it doubtful whether a small quantity of elements of the tin-group is present. In any such doubtful case the analyst should compare the precipitate obtained with that produced by acidifying an equal portion of the pure Na_2S reagent and shaking the mixture. If the conclusion is still uncertain, the HCl precipitate is treated by the last paragraph of this Procedure.

6. The conclusion as to the presence of a small quantity of the tin-group becomes more uncertain in case the sulfide solution contains a little copper or bismuth, whose sulfides are slightly soluble in the reagent (as stated in Note 5, P. 22); for then the precipitate may have a dark orange or a dark yellow color. It is therefore directed to treat the HCl precipitate with NH_4OH, so as to separate any arsenic, antimony, and tin from the sulfur, whenever these elements are present in quantity (1–2 mg.) not sufficient to give a pronounced yellow or orange color to the precipitate, and when not enough mercury is present to give a distinct black color to the precipitate. It may be mentioned, moreover, that a mixture of SnS_2 and Sb_2S_5 does not always have a color intermediate between the yellow and orange colors of the separate sulfides, but that it may be brown or dark gray.

7. By the treatment of the HCl precipitate with NH_4OH the excess of sulfur and any HgS, CuS, or Bi_2S_3 present is left undissolved (or is reprecipitated by the $(NH_4)_2S$ added to the solution), so that the second HCl precipitate can contain only sulfides of arsenic, antimony, and tin and a very little sulfur. As_2S_5 dissolves abundantly in NH_4OH, and Sb_2S_5 and SnS_2 in moderate quantity, owing to the formation of a mixture of salts of partially sulfurated acids, such as H_3AsO_3S and $H_3AsO_2S_2$. The addition of $(NH_4)_2S$ to the NH_4OH solution and the heating serve to convert these into salts of the fully sulfurated acids, such as H_3AsS_4; from which HCl will then precipitate the simple sulfides much more completely.

ANALYSIS OF THE COPPER-GROUP

TABLE V. — ANALYSIS OF THE COPPER-GROUP.

Residue from the Sodium Sulfide Treatment: PbS, Bi₂S₃, CuS, CdS.
Boil with HNO₃ (P. 31).

Solution: Pb, Bi, Cu, Cd as nitrates.
Add H₂SO₄, evaporate, add water (P. 32).

Precipitate: PbSO₄. *Dissolve in NH₄Ac, add K₂CrO₄ (P. 33).*	Filtrate. *Add NH₄OH (P. 34).*			
	Precipitate: Bi(OH)₃. *Add Na₂SnO₂ (P. 35).*	Filtrate: Cu(NH₃)₄SO₄, Cd(NH₃)₄SO₄.		
		To a small part add HAc and K₄Fe(CN)₆ (P. 36).	*To the remainder add H₂SO₄ and Fe (P. 37).*	
Yellow precipitate: PbCrO₄.	Black residue: Bi.		Precipitate: Cu.	Solution: CdSO₄. *Add H₂S.*
		Red precipitate: Cu₂Fe(CN)₆. White precipitate: Cd₂Fe(CN)₆.		Yellow precipitate: CdS.

Procedure 31. — *Solution of the Sulfides in Nitric Acid.* — Transfer the residue from the Na₂S treatment (P. 22) to a casserole, and add 5–15 cc. of 3 n. HNO₃. Stir the mixture, boil it gently for 2–3 minutes, and filter it. (Residue, see Note 3; solution, P. 32.)

Notes. — 1. Boiling 3 n. HNO₃ dissolves the sulfides very much more rapidly than HCl or H₂SO₄ of the same concentration; for with the latter acids the sulfide-ion is removed from the solution only by combination with the hydrogen-ion and by the volatization of the H₂S formed thereby, while with HNO₃ the sulfide-ion and the H₂S in equilibrium with it may also be destroyed by oxidation to ordinary sulfur. The oxidizing action of HNO₃ is, however, slow, unless it is hot and at least as concentrated as 2 normal. Some sulfur is always oxidized to H_2SO_4 by the boiling HNO_3; but, even in the presence of much lead, $PbSO_4$ is not precipitated, owing to its moderate solubility in HNO_3.

2. When much lead, copper, or bismuth is present the sulfur formed may enclose enough of the undissolved sulfide to give it a black color; but the heating need not be continued till the residue becomes light colored.

3. In case it is desired to detect as little as 2 mg. of mercury in the presence of a large quantity of copper or cadmium, the residue undissolved by HNO_3 should be treated by P. 43.

Procedure 32. — *Precipitation of Lead.* — To the HNO_3 solution (P. 31) add 3 cc. of 18 n. H_2SO_4, and evaporate in a casserole till dense white fumes of H_2SO_4 begin to come off, adding 2 cc. more of 18 n. H_2SO_4 if a large residue separates during the evaporation. Cool the mixture, and pour it, a little at a time, into 10 cc. of cold water in a test-tube, cooling the tube after each addition. Finally rinse out the casserole with the same solution, cool the mixture, and let it stand 5 minutes, but not much longer. (Fine white precipitate, presence of LEAD.) Filter, and wash the precipitate first with 2 n. H_2SO_4, and then with about 5 cc. of water. (Precipitate, P. 33; filtrate, P. 34.)

Notes. — 1. The solution is evaporated with H_2SO_4 in order to expel the HNO_3, which if not removed would dissolve some $PbSO_4$ and diminish the delicacy of the test for lead. The fact that the presence of HNO_3 increases the solubility of $PbSO_4$ in water is due to the formation by metathesis of the intermediate ion HSO_4^-, which has a much smaller ionization tendency than HNO_3 or H_2SO_4, as will be seen from the Table of Ionization Values in the Appendix.

2. A fairly large quantity of H_2SO_4 is added, so as to diminish the solubility of $PbSO_4$, which it does in virtue of the common-ion effect and so as to hold even a large quantity of bismuth in solution.

3. The mixture is allowed to stand a few minutes so as to insure complete precipitation of the lead; for the solutions of crystalline substances, like $PbSO_4$, tend to remain supersaturated. It is not allowed to stand longer; for otherwise, when much bismuth is present, it may separate as a coarsely crystalline precipitate of $(BiO)_2SO_4$, to such extent that not more than 50 mg. of bismuth remain in solution.

4. It is with the purpose of holding a large quantity of bismuth in solution in the supersaturated condition that special care is also taken to keep the mixture cool during the dilution of the H_2SO_4; for heating tends to break up the state of saturation.

5. If in spite of these precautions a large coarsely crystalline precipitate separates, it should, before applying the confirmatory test for lead, be dissolved in 5–10 cc. of HCl, and the solution treated again by P. 32. The smaller quantity of bismuth now present in the solution is not likely to precipitate on diluting the H_2SO_4 solution with water. Any $PbSO_4$ present is dissolved by the HCl; and this acid must be all evaporated off to insure complete reprecipitation of the lead.

Procedure 33. — *Confirmatory Test for Lead.* — Pour repeatedly through the filter containing the H_2SO_4 precipitate (P. 32) a 5–15 cc. portion of 3 n. NH_4Ac (ammonium acetate) solution. (See Note 1, P. 12.) To the filtrate add 2–5 drops of 3 n. K_2CrO_4 solution and 2–5 cc. of HAc (acetic acid). (Yellow precipitate, presence of LEAD.)

Notes. — 1. This confirmatory test for lead should not be omitted; for the H_2SO_4 precipitate may consist not only of $PbSO_4$ but of $(BiO)_2SO_4$ or of $BaSO_4$, which last closely resembles $PbSO_4$ in appearance. $(BiO)_2SO_4$ dissolves in NH_4Ac solution, and gives a yellow precipitate on adding K_2CrO_4; but this precipitate, unlike $PbCrO_4$, dissolves readily in HAc. $BaSO_4$ is not dissolved by NH_4Ac solution.

2. The solubility of $PbSO_4$ in NH_4Ac solution depends on the formation by metathesis of unionized $PbAc_2$, this salt being much less ionized than most other salts of the same valence-type. (See the Table of Ionization Values in the Appendix.) On the addition of K_2CrO_4 to this solution the much less soluble $PbCrO_4$ is precipitated.

Procedure 34. — *Precipitation of Bismuth.* — Make the H_2SO_4 solution (P. 32) alkaline with NH_4OH (see Note 1). (White precipitate, presence of BISMUTH; blue solution, presence of COPPER.) Filter, and wash the precipitate thoroughly (see Note 1, P. 21). (Precipitate, P. 35; filtrate, P. 36 and 37.)

Notes. — 1. *Whenever a solution is to be made alkaline with NH_4OH, the reagent may be added, first in quantity nearly equivalent to the acid known to be present, then 10–15 drops at a time, till a distinct odor of NH_4OH is perceptible after shaking the mixture so as to make sure that none of the reagent is left on the sides of the flask.*

2. The precipitate produced by NH_4OH may consist of $Fe(OH)_3$ or of other hydroxides of the iron-group, if these elements were not removed from the H_2S precipitate by thorough washing. The formation of a small precipitate is, therefore, not a sufficient proof of the presence of bismuth; and the confirmatory test of P. 35 must be applied.

3. $Cd(OH)_2$ or $Cu(OH)_2$, though only very slightly soluble in water, dissolves in NH_4OH owing to the combination of the Cd^{++} or Cu^{++} ion with NH_3, forming the complex cation $Cd(NH_3)_4{}^{++}$ or $Cu(NH_3)_4{}^{++}$. These complex cations have an extremely small ionization tendency; thus in a normal NH_4OH solution the ratio of the concentration of the complex cadmium ion to the simple cadmium ion is about 10^7.

Procedure 35. — *Confirmatory Test for Bismuth.* — Pour through the filter containing the well-washed NH_4OH precipitate (P. 34) a cold freshly prepared solution of Na_2SnO_2 (sodium stannite) (see Note 1). (Immediate blackening of the residue, presence of BISMUTH.)

Notes. — 1. The solution of sodium stannite (Na_2SnO_2) is prepared when needed by adding NaOH solution, a few drops at a time, to 8–10 drops of $SnCl_2$ reagent diluted with 3 cc. of water (the mixture being cooled in running water after each addition), till the large precipitate of $Sn(OH)_2$ first formed is dissolved and a clear or slightly turbid liquid results. The solution must be kept cold while it is being prepared, and it must be freshly prepared, because the stannite decomposes spontaneously into stannate (Na_2SnO_3) and metallic Sn, and because it oxidizes in contact with air to sodium stannate. SnO_2H_2 is an example of a so-called amphoteric substance — one which acts either as a base or an acid, as is shown by its solubility in both acids and alkalies.

2. The final test with Na_2SnO_2 depends on the reduction of $Bi(OH)_3$ to black metallic Bi. The test is an extremely delicate one. The other reducible substances, like $HSbO_3$, $Fe(OH)_3$, $Pb(OH)_2$, or $Cu(OH)_2$, that might possibly be present in the NH_4OH precipitate are not reduced by short contact with Na_2SnO_2 solution in the cold. Mercury, if present, would cause blackening; but it is not precipitated by NH_4OH in the presence of ammonium salt.

Procedure 36. — *Confirmatory Test for Copper.* — Acidify one-fourth of the NH_4OH solution (P. 34) with HAc, add from a dropper one drop of $K_4Fe(CN)_6$ solution, and let the mixture stand 2–3 minutes. Then add 3 cc. more of $K_4Fe(CN)_6$ solution. (Red precipitate, presence of COPPER.)

Notes. — 1. The confirmatory test for copper is more delicate than the formation of a blue color with NH_4OH (P. 34). It should, therefore, be tried even when the NH_4OH solution is colorless. Cadmium is also precipitated by $K_4Fe(CN)_6$; but the precipitate is white, and does not prevent the pink color of the copper compound from being detected, provided only a small quantity of $K_4Fe(CN)_6$ is added, and the mixture is allowed to stand; for the copper salt, owing to its smaller solubility, is precipitated immediately or formed rapidly by metathesis from the precipitated $Cd_2Fe(CN)_6$.

Procedure 37. — *Detection of Cadmium.* — To the remainder of the NH_4OH solution (P. 34) add H_2SO_4, 1 cc. at a time, till the solution reddens litmus paper, and then 5 cc. more. Heat the mixture to 50–60°, add to it about 1 cc. of iron powder (see Note 1), and shake the mixture gently for about two minutes. (If much copper is present, add ½ cc. of iron powder and 2 cc. of H_2SO_4, and shake the mixture a minute longer). Pour it through a filter; add to the filtrate 20 cc. of water (and, if it is turbid, a few drops of H_2SO_4); and saturate it in a flash immediately with H_2S. (Yellow precipitate, presence of CADMIUM.)

Notes. — 1. In case copper is entirely absent (as shown by P. 36), the Fe powder need not be added, and the NH_4OH solution may be slightly acidified with H_2SO_4 and saturated directly with H_2S.

2. The rate at which the copper is precipitated by the iron, like that of all reactions between solid substances and solutions, increases with the temperature and with the surface of contact between the solid and the solution. The copper is completely precipitated within two minutes when 1 cc. of iron in finely powdered form is used, and when the warm solution is steadily shaken with it.

3. The filtrate from the Fe treatment is saturated with H_2S immediately, since otherwise the $FeSO_4$ present will be oxidized by the air to the ferric state, and produce with the H_2S a precipitate of sulfur.

4. In case H_2S produces a black precipitate, owing to the incomplete removal of the copper by the Fe powder or to the presence of mercury (in case Fe powder was not added), heat it with 5–10 cc. of 3 n. HNO_3, evaporate the solution with 2 cc. of 18 n. H_2SO_4 till dense white fumes appear, dilute the solution with 15 cc. of water, treat it with Fe powder as in P. 37, filter, and saturate the filtrate with H_2S. By this treatment any copper or mercury is removed; and a yellow precipitate will then be produced by H_2S if cadmium is present.

5. In case a yellow precipitate is produced by H_2S, and the substance contains much arsenic, antimony, or tin (as shown by P. 44–47), it is well to prove that the H_2S precipitate does not arise from one of these elements by washing it thoroughly with hot water, and pouring repeatedly through the filter containing it a 10 cc. portion of hot

NH_4OH. This dissolves As_2S_5, Sb_2S_5, and SnS_2; but leaves CdS as a yellow residue on the filter.

6. The principles determining whether a metal will precipitate another metal from solutions of its salts are as follows. Of two given elements that one will precipitate the other whose " reduction-potential" is the greater. The value of the reduction-potential of an element is determined by a constant characteristic of the metal and by the concentration of its ion in the solution. The constants (expressed in volts and referred to that of hydrogen gas against hydrogen-ion taken as zero) characteristic of the more important elements are given in the Table in the Appendix. These characteristic constants, which are called the molal reduction-potentials of the elements, are so evaluated as to represent the actual reduction-potentials of the respective metals when the concentration of their ions is 1 molal. Thus 0.12 volt is the reduction-potential of lead when the Pb^{++} ion in the solution has a concentration of 1 molal. The actual reduction-potential of a metallic element becomes greater by a definite amount for each ten-fold decrease in its ion-concentration; namely, by 0.06 volt if the ion is univalent, by 0.03 volt if it is bivalent, and by 0.02 volt if it is trivalent. Thus the reduction-potential of lead is 0.18 volt when the Pb^{++} ion-concentration is 0.01 molal.

7. These principles may be applied to the separation of copper and cadmium by means of iron as follows. Referring to the table we see that the molal reduction-potentials of iron and copper are $+0.44$ and -0.34 volt, respectively. Owing to the fact that the iron rapidly dissolves in the H_2SO_4 solution, we may as a rough approximation consider that the ferrous-ion concentration is 1 molal, and therefore that the actual reduction-potential of the iron is equal to its molal reduction-potential, $+0.44$ volt. The reduction-potential of the copper will increase from the molal value -0.34 by 0.03 volt each time the concentration of the copper-ion is decreased ten-fold; thus it will be -0.31 when the copper-ion is 0.1 molal, -0.28 when it is 0.01 molal, -0.25 when it is 0.001 molal, etc. Evidently, it will continue to be less than that of the iron ($+0.44$) until the copper-ion falls to the extremely low concentration of 10^{-26} molal. Hence substantially all the copper will be precipitated. On the other hand, in case of the cadmium, whose molal reduction-potential is $+0.40$, its actual reduction-potential becomes nearly equal to that of the iron when its concentration becomes 0.1 molal. Since even 500 mg. of cadmium in a volume of 40 cc. corresponds to a cadmium-ion concentration somewhat less than 0.1 molal, no cadmium will be precipitated by the iron under the actual conditions.

ANALYSIS OF THE TIN-GROUP

TABLE VI. — ANALYSIS OF THE TIN-GROUP.

Precipitate from Sodium Sulfide Solution: S, HgS, As₂S₅, Sb₂S₅, SnS₂. *Heat with 12 n. HCl (P. 41).*			
Residue: S, HgS, As₂S₅. *Add NH₄OH (P. 42).*		Solution: SbCl₃, H₂SnCl₆. *Dilute, heat, pass in H₂S (P. 45).*	
Residue: S, HgS. *Add HCl and KClO₃ (P. 43).*	Solution. *Evaporate, add HNO₃, then NH₄OH (P. 44).*	Orange precipitate: Sb₂S₃. *Dissolve in HCl, add Sn (P. 46).*	Solution: H₂SnCl₆. *Partly neutralize, pass in H₂S (P. 47).*
Solution: HgCl₂. *Add SnCl₂.*	Solution: (NH₄)₃AsO₄. *Add Mg(NO₃)₂.*	Black deposit: Sb. *Add NaOBr.*	Precipitate: SnS₂. *Evaporate without filtering (P. 47).*
Precipitate: Hg₂Cl₂ or Hg.	Precipitate: MgNH₄AsO₄. *Add AgNO₃.*	Black deposit: Sb.	Solution: H₂SnCl₆. *Boil with Sb.*
	Red residue: Ag₃AsO₄.		Solution: SnCl₂. *Add HgCl₂.*
			Precipitate: Hg₂Cl₂.

Procedure 41. — *Separation of Arsenic and Mercury from Antimony and Tin.* — Transfer the precipitated sulfides dried by suction (P. 23) to a test-tube, add from a small graduate exactly 10 cc. of 12 n. HCl, place the test-tube in a small beaker of water, heat the water till the contents of the tube begin to bubble, and keep the water for ten minutes at a temperature which causes only slight bubbling in the tube, stirring its contents from time to time. Then pass a slow current of H₂S into the tube (still kept in the hot water-bath) for one minute. Add gradually with stirring 3 cc. of water, and filter the hot mixture with the aid of suction through a dry filter or one wet with 6 n. HCl. Remove the filtrate, and wash the residue first with 6 n. HCl, then with hot water. (Residue, P. 42; solution, P. 45.)

Use Marsh Test for arsenic.

Notes. — 1. If a much weaker HCl solution than the acid of 12 normal concentration is used, or if the acid becomes diluted by an unnecessary quantity of water left in the precipitate, much Sb_2S_5 will be left undissolved. Even with the strong acid some Sb_2S_5 may remain undissolved, especially when a large quantity is present, in which case the residue if small in amount will have an orange color. This small quantity of Sb_2S_5 would be only very slowly removed by further treatments with HCl; it does not, however, interfere with the subsequent tests for arsenic. Moreover, when only a small quantity of Sb_2S_5 is originally present, a large proportion of it is extracted, so that it will not escape detection. Sb_2S_5 dissolves with formation of $SbCl_3$, the element being reduced from the antimonic state by the H_2S with liberation of sulfur; SnS_2 dissolves with formation of $SnCl_4$, which unites with the excess of HCl to form H_2SnCl_6.

2. If the solution be heated so that only slight bubbling occurs during the treatment with HCl, the amount of As_2S_5 which dissolves in ten minutes is insignificant. But this is no longer true if the solution be allowed to boil rapidly; for the boiling expels from the solution the H_2S liberated from the other sulfides or by slight decomposition of the As_2S_5 itself, and thus enables the decomposition of the latter to proceed further. As a precaution, the mixture is finally saturated with H_2S to reprecipitate any arsenic or mercury that may have passed into solution; for, if not so removed, it would come down later with the antimony (in P. 45), and might be mistaken for it.

3. About 3 cc. of water are gradually added to the HCl solution to enable it to be filtered. If more is added, Sb_2S_3 may precipitate. If this happens after the filtration, it does no harm.

4. Care must be taken to follow closely the directions in regard to the quantity of HCl used and to avoid any loss of the solution in the filtration; for the subsequent separation of antimony and tin (in P. 45) depends upon a proper concentration of the acid.

5. The greater part of any CuS and Bi_2S_3 present is dissolved by the HCl. The copper will be precipitated later with the antimony (in P. 45), and the bismuth with the tin (in P. 47). A little copper remains with the As_2S_5, but this does not interfere with the tests for arsenic.

Procedure 42. — *Separation of Arsenic from Mercury.* — Transfer to a casserole (see Note 1, P. 22) the residue undissolved by HCl (P. 41). Warm it with 5–15 cc. of NH_4OH for 2–3 minutes with frequent agitation, and filter the mixture. (Dark colored residue, presence of MERCURY.) Wash the residue. (Residue, P. 43; solution, P. 44.)

Notes.— 1. By this treatment with NH_4OH 1 mg. of arsenic can be extracted from a residue containing even 500 mg. of mercury. But when the residue consists only of sulfur and 1–3 mg. of arsenic, most of the arsenic may be left with the sulfur, mechanically enclosed in it. Enough arsenic is, however, usually extracted to enable it to be detected in P. 44, provided care be taken to use in that Procedure the minimum quantities of reagent.

2. As to the chemical action of NH_4OH on As_2S_5, see Note 7, P. 23.

Procedure 43. — *Detection of Mercury.* — Transfer the residue undissolved by NH_4OH (P. 42) to a casserole, add 3–8 cc. of HCl, heat the mixture nearly to boiling, and add to it powdered $KClO_3$, a little at a time, till the black residue disappears. Boil the solution till it no longer smells of chlorine, replacing the acid which evaporates. Add to it 5–10 cc. of water, and filter out the residue. To the filtrate add from a dropper 1–2 drops of $SnCl_2$ solution, then 2–5 cc. more. (White precipitate turning gray, or gray precipitate, presence of MERCURY.)

Notes.— 1. A mixture of HCl and $KClO_3$ is used to dissolve the HgS, since it is one of the few sulfides that is very slowly attacked by HCl or HNO_3 alone. It can most easily be brought into solution with the aid of free Cl_2; and a mixture of HCl and HNO_3, which by their action upon one another produce Cl_2, might be used. But the $KClO_3$ has the advantage that an unnecessary excess can be easily avoided, and any free Cl_2 in the solution can be quickly expelled by boiling the solution. The main product of the reaction between $KClO_3$ and HCl is Cl_2; but some ClO_2 is also formed, which gives the yellow color to the solution.

2. That HgS, unlike most other sulfides, does not dissolve readily in even fairly concentrated HCl or HNO_3 is doubtless due to the much smaller concentration of its ions in its saturated solution and to the fact that at this small concentration sulfide-ion (or the H_2S in equilibrium with it at a correspondingly small concentration) is oxidized only very slowly even by the HNO_3. HgS is, however, readily dissolved by Cl_2, a more vigorous oxidizing agent, since it reacts rapidly with sulfide-ion (or with H_2S) even when its concentration is very small.

3. Only one or two drops of $SnCl_2$ solution are added at first, so as to cause the precipitation of white Hg_2Cl_2. An excess of $SnCl_2$ is then added, so as to convert this white precipitate into a fine gray precipitate of metallic Hg, this darkening being especially characteristic of mercury. Moreover, if the Cl_2 was not completely expelled from

the solution, it will oxidize the $SnCl_2$ contained in the first drop or two of solution added.

4. In case a large quantity (200–500 mg.) of copper or cadmium is present, mercury in quantities up to 2–3 mg. may escape detection, owing to its being retained in the copper-group residue, as stated in Note 5, P. 22. In such a case, the residue left undissolved by HNO_3 in P. 31 should be tested for mercury by treating it by this Procedure.

Procedure 44. — *Detection of Arsenic.* — Evaporate the NH_4OH solution (P. 42) almost to dryness (see Note 2, P. 21). Add 2–5 cc. of HNO_3, and heat the mixture nearly to boiling till the residue dissolves or only sulfur remains. Evaporate the mixture almost to dryness, add 1–3 cc. of water and 1–3 cc. of NH_4OH, filter out any residue, add to the solution in a test-tube 3–10 cc. of $Mg(NO_3)_2$ reagent, shake the mixture, and let it stand 10–15 minutes with occasional shaking. (White crystalline precipitate, presence of ARSENIC.)

Filter, wash the precipitate with 2–3 cc. of water, and pour over it on the filter 1 cc. of $AgNO_3$ solution to which 6–8 drops of HAc have been added. (Dark red residue, presence of ARSENIC.)

Notes. — 1. After the NH_4OH is expelled by the evaporation, the As_2S_5 (together with any Sb_2S_5 present) is thrown down as a yellow or orange-colored precipitate. This furnishes a fairly delicate indication of the presence of arsenic, except that any antimony left in the residue undissolved by HCl will also give an orange precipitate. The precipitate, without filtering it off, is redissolved by HNO_3, which has a sufficiently strong oxidizing action to convert As_2S_5 into H_3AsO_4.

2. The precipitate of $Mg(NH_4)AsO_4$, because of its tendency to hydrolyze into NH_4OH and $Mg^{++}HAsO_4^-$, is more soluble in water than in the NH_4OH solution. Its solubility is also diminished by the excess of $Mg(NO_3)_2$ reagent, in virtue of the common-ion effect. Since the precipitate, like other crystalline substances, tends to form a supersaturated solution, the mixture is allowed to stand with occasional shaking.

3. The reagent used for the precipitation is a solution 1 n. in $Mg(NO_3)_2$, 3 n. in NH_4NO_3, and 0.2 n. in NH_4OH. The NH_4NO_3, by reducing the hydroxide-ion concentration, prevents the precipitation of $Mg(OH)_2$ by the NH_4OH. A little NH_4OH is added to the reagent to remove any iron, aluminum, or other impurity that may be present in the magnesium or ammonium salt. The nitrates are used, rather

than the chlorides, so as not to produce a precipitate of AgCl in the confirmatory test with $AgNO_3$.

4. The $AgNO_3$ added in the confirmatory test converts the $Mg(NH_4)AsO_4$ into dark red Ag_3AsO_4, since the latter compound has a much smaller solubility-product. HAc is added to neutralize the NH_4OH; for otherwise this might prevent the precipitation of the Ag_3AsO_4, by forming the complex silver-ammonia ion. The test serves to distinguish $Mg(NH_4)AsO_4$ from $Mg(OH)_2$ or any other hydroxide that might be precipitated by NH_4OH.

Procedure 45. — *Separation of Antimony and Tin.* — Dilute the solution from the HCl treatment of the sulfides (P. 41) with water to a volume of just 55 cc., transfer it to a flask placed in a 400 cc. beaker of boiling water, and after the solution has become hot pass into it a moderate current of H_2S gas for 8–10 minutes but not longer, keeping the water in the beaker gently boiling. (Orange-red precipitate, presence of ANTIMONY.) Filter while hot, using suction if the precipitate is large, and wash the precipitate with hot water. (Precipitate, P. 46; filtrate, P. 47.)

Notes. — 1. By following carefully the directions given in P. 41 and in this Procedure, a good separation of antimony and tin may be obtained; thus, when only 1 mg. of antimony is present it is precipitated, while (stannic) tin gives no precipitate, unless 400–500 mg. are present. If, however, the HCl solution be more concentrated, a small quantity of antimony will escape detection. On the other hand, if the HCl solution be more dilute, or if it be not kept hot, much SnS_2 may precipitate when a large amount of tin is present. When SnS_2 is mixed with a little Sb_2S_3 a brown precipitate results.

2. If copper be present in the substance, a little CuS may separate at this point as a black precipitate.

3. Owing to the possibility that substances other than antimony may be precipitated by H_2S in this Procedure, the confirmatory test described in P. 46 must always be applied to any precipitate obtained. The quantity of antimony present can, however, usually be better estimated from the size of the H_2S precipitate than from that of the black deposit obtained in the confirmatory test.

Procedure 46. — *Confirmatory Test for Antimony.* — Transfer the H_2S precipitate (P. 45) to a small casserole, heat it with 2–5 cc. of 12 n. HCl, add 2–5 cc. of water, filter, and evaporate the filtrate to about 2 cc. Cool the solution, and place in it a flat piece of bright mossy tin. After 5–10 minutes pour off the liquid, wash the residue carefully with water by decantation, and pour over it 2 cc. of fresh NaOBr (sodium hypobromite) reagent (see Note 3). (Black residue remaining undissolved, presence of ANTIMONY.)

Notes. — 1. Tin, rather than a more reducing metal like zinc, is used in precipitating the antimony, since such a metal would also precipitate tin from the solution. The small quantity of copper that may be present is also precipitated by the tin; but antimony is readily distinguished by its coal-black color (given even by 0.1–0.2 mg.) from a red or brownish-black one of copper. Arsenic, if present, is also precipitated on the tin or in the solution; but it is distinguished from antimony by its behavior with NaOBr solution. These facts as to the precipitation of the metals are explained by the values of their molal reduction-potentials (given in the Table in the Appendix). These differ so greatly from that of tin as to make consideration of the ion-concentrations, which are complicated in the cases of antimony and arsenic, of secondary importance.

2. The treatment with NaOBr solution serves to prove that the black precipitate is not arsenic; for this element is readily converted by this reagent into arsenate, while antimony (as well as copper) is not attacked by it.

3. Since hypobromite solution rapidly decomposes, with formation of bromate and bromide, the reagent should be prepared when needed by adding to 2 cc. of saturated Br_2 solution, NaOH solution, drop by drop, till the solution becomes colorless or yellow, and then adding as many drops more of NaOH solution.

Procedure 47. — *Detection of Tin.* — To the filtrate from the H_2S precipitate (P. 45) add just 4 cc. of 15 n. NH_4OH, cool the mixture, saturate it with H_2S, cork the flask, and let it stand for 10 minutes. (Yellowish turbidity or yellow flocculent precipitate, presence of TIN.)

In case H_2S has produced a precipitate, evaporate the mixture (without filtering it) in a casserole to 15–20 cc., or further, if the precipitate has not dissolved. Add $\frac{1}{2}$ cc. of powdered antimony, and boil the mixture gently for 2–3 minutes. Filter, and to the filtrate add at once 2–3 cc. of HCl and 10 cc. of 0.2 n. $HgCl_2$ solution. (White or gray precipitate, presence of TIN.)

Notes. — 1. The acid present is partially neutralized with NH_4OH and the solution is cooled, in order to diminish the solubility of SnS_2. Time is allowed for the precipitation, because stannic tin reacts more slowly with H_2S than most of the other elements, doubtless because the tin exists mainly in the HCl solution as $H^+_2SnCl_6^-$, and not as Sn^{++++} ion. When only a small quantity (0.5 to 2 mg.) of tin is present, the precipitate of SnS_2 produces in the solution a yellowish translucent turbidity, which is readily distinguished from the trace of finely divided sulfur which may separate.

2. In the confirmatory test the precipitate of SnS_2 is not filtered off, but is dissolved by concentrating the acid by evaporation, since it clogs the filter and also tends to pass through it. The $HgCl_2$ reagent is added to the solution as soon as it is filtered from the antimony, since $SnCl_2$ oxidizes rapidly in the air. The HCl is added to prevent the precipitation of SbOCl.

3. Metallic antimony is used, rather than zinc or iron, to reduce the tin from the stannic to the stannous condition, since antimony does not reduce the tin to the metallic state and since it is only slowly dissolved by boiling HCl.

4. Just as metals with respect to conversion into their ions can be arranged in a series in the order of their reducing power and assigned certain values, the molal reduction-potentials, expressing this power quantitatively, so reducing substances in solution, like stannous or ferrous salts, can with respect to their conversion into a higher state of oxidation, thus into stannic or ferric salts, be included in the same series with appropriate values of the molal reduction-potentials. Such molal reduction-potentials represent the actual reduction-potentials when the concentrations of both the ions involved (thus of Sn^{++++} and Sn^{++}, or of Fe^{+++} and Fe^{++}) are equal. For each ten-fold decrease in the ratio of the concentration of the ion of higher valence to that of the ion of lower valence, the actual potential increases by 0.06 volt, if the difference in the two valences is unity (as in the case of Fe^{++}, Fe^{+++}), or by 0.03 volt if the valence difference is two (as in the case of Sn^{++}, Sn^{++++}).

DETECTION OF PHOSPHATE

Procedure 50. — *Detection of Phosphate.* — Boil 5 cc. of the filtrate from the H_2S precipitate (P. 21) till the H_2S is expelled, pour it into a mixture of 5 cc. of HNO_3 and 5 cc. of $(NH_4)_2MoO_4$ reagent, heat the mixture to 60–70°, and let it stand for 5–10 minutes. (Fine yellow precipitate, presence of PHOSPHATE.) Reject the mixture.

Notes. — 1. Phosphate is tested for here, since its presence may cause the precipitation of the alkaline-earth elements (as phosphates) with the aluminum- and iron-groups (see Note 6, P. 51) and thus make it necessary to modify somewhat the method of analysis of the iron-group. The test is made after the H_2S precipitation, since arsenate might yield a similar precipitate. Incidentally the test makes it unnecessary to provide for the detection of phosphate in the process for the Detection of the Acidic Constituents.

2. The precipitate produced is the triammonium salt of a complex phosphomolybdic acid, $H^+_3PO_4(MoO_3)_{12}^\equiv$. Large quantities of $(NH_4)_2MoO_4$ and HNO_3 are added, so as to convert the $PO_4^\equiv$ ion to a large extent into the complex anion. A large quantity of NH_4NO_3 is also added, so as to diminish the solubility of the ammonium phosphomolybdate, which it does in virtue of the common-ion effect. The NH_4NO_3 is added with the reagent itself, which is a solution 1 normal in $(NH_4)_2MoO_4$ and 3 normal in NH_4NO_3. The mixture is warmed, so as to increase the rate of formation of the complex anion. It is not boiled, since too high a temperature may cause the precipitation of white MoO_3 from the acidified reagent.

3. Under these conditions $\frac{1}{40}$ mg. of phosphate (PO_4) can be detected in the 5 cc. of solution tested, corresponding to $\frac{1}{2}$ mg. of it in the whole solution.

PRECIPITATION AND SEPARATION OF THE ALUMINUM AND
IRON GROUPS.

TABLE VII. — PRECIPITATION AND SEPARATION OF THE ALUMINUM AND
IRON GROUPS.

Filtrate from the Hydrogen Sulfide Precipitate.	
Add NH_4OH in excess (P. 51).	

Precipitate*: $Al(OH)_3$, $Cr(OH)_3$, $Fe(OH)_{2-3}$; $Mn(OH)_3$ after exposure to air.
Solution: Salts of $Zn(NH_3)_4$, $Ni(NH_3)_4$, Co, Mn, Ba, Sr, Ca, Mg, K, and Na.
    Add $(NH_4)_2S$ and filter (P. 51).

Precipitate*: $Al(OH)_3$, $Cr(OH)_3$, FeS, ZnS, MnS, CoS, NiS. *Dissolve in HCl and $KClO_3$, add NaOH (P. 52).*	Filtrate: ALKALINE- EARTH and ALKALI GROUPS.
Precipitate*: $Fe(OH)_3$, $Mn(OH)_2$, $Co(OH)_2$, $Ni(OH)_2$. Solution: $NaAlO_2$, $NaCrO_2$, Na_2ZnO_2. *Add Na_2O_2 and filter (P. 52).*	

Filtrate: ALUMINUM-GROUP. $NaAlO_2$, Na_2ZnO_2, Na_2CrO_4. See Table VIII.	Precipitate*: IRON-GROUP. $MnO(OH)_2$, $Fe(OH)_3$, $Co(OH)_3$, $Ni(OH)_2$. See Table IX.

*When phosphate is present in the solution, these precipitates may contain the phosphates of the elements otherwise precipitated as hydroxides, and also the phosphates of barium, strontium, calcium, and magnesium.

Procedure 51. — *Precipitation of the Aluminum and Iron Groups.* — Boil the remainder of the filtrate from the H_2S precipitate (P. 21) till the H_2S is expelled, make it alkaline with NH_4OH (see Note 1, P. 34), and heat the mixture to boiling. (No precipitate, absence of ALUMINUM, CHROMIUM, IRON, and ALKALINE-EARTH PHOSPHATE.)   Add 6 n. $(NH_4)_2S$ solution, 1 cc. at a time (or if nickel seems to be present, pass in H_2S a minute at a time), till after shaking the flask the vapors slightly darken paper moistened with $PbAc_2$ solution.   Heat the mixture nearly to boiling, shake it, and let it stand 2 or 3 minutes.   (Precipitate, presence of ALUMINUM-GROUP or IRON-GROUP or of ALKALINE-EARTH PHOSPHATE.)   Filter, using suction if the precipitate is

large, and wash the precipitate, first with water containing about
1% of the $(NH_4)_2S$ solution, and then with a little pure water.
If the filtration is slow, keep the funnel covered with a watch-
glass. To the filtrate add a few drops of $(NH_4)_2S$ solution,
and boil the mixture for a few seconds (or, in case it is dark
colored, until it becomes colorless or light yellow); filter out
any precipitate, uniting it with the preceding one. (Precipitate,
P. 52; filtrate, P. 71.)

Notes. — 1. The purposes of the various operations are as follows:
The H_2S is boiled out so that the effect of the addition of NH_4OH alone
may be noted; for it often gives useful indications as to what elements
are present or absent. Only a slight excess of $(NH_4)_2S$ is used, in
order to prevent so far as possible dissolving NiS. By passing H_2S
into the ammoniacal solution, instead of adding $(NH_4)_2S$, the dissolving
of NiS may be almost entirely prevented; therefore, though the
operation takes a little longer, the use of H_2S is to be preferred when
nickel seems to be present. The mixture is shaken in order to coagulate
the precipitate and make it filter more readily. The heating also
promotes the coagulation of the precipitate. To the filtrate a few
drops of the $(NH_4)_2S$ solution are added to make sure an excess is
present. The filtrate is boiled for a few moments to insure the complete precipitation of $Cr(OH)_3$, or longer to insure that of NiS, whose
presence is indicated by a brown or nearly black color of the filtrate.
Finally, it is directed to wash with water containing a little $(NH_4)_2S$
and to keep the filter covered, in order that some excess of $(NH_4)_2S$
may always be present; for, if the $(NH_4)_2S$ adhering to the precipitate
is removed by oxidation or by volatilization (as H_2S and NH_3), the
sulfides are oxidized to soluble sulfates by the air. If suction is used,
for the same reason care must be taken not to suck air through the
precipitate.

2. By a moderate excess of NH_4OH in the presence of ammonium
salt the trivalent elements, aluminum, chromium, and ferric iron, are
completely precipitated; while the bivalent elements, zinc, manganese,
nickel, cobalt, ferrous iron, and the alkaline-earth elements, remain
in solution (except that when a large quantity of cobalt is present, it
may be partially precipitated as a basic salt). Ferrous and manganous
salts are, however, rapidly oxidized in alkaline solution by the oxygen
of the air; and the higher hydroxides are then precipitated. Cobaltous
salts in ammoniacal solution are also oxidized by the air; but the
cobaltic hydroxide remains in solution. When chromium is present,

zinc and magnesium may be completely precipitated in combination with it as chromites ($ZnCrO_2$ and $MgCrO_2$). If a large excess of NH_4OH is used, a few milligrams of aluminum and chromium may be dissolved, the latter in larger quantity if the mixture be not heated to boiling.

3. In view of these facts, the conclusion may be drawn that aluminum, chromium, and iron are absent in case the NH_4OH does not produce a precipitate that is perceptible even after heating the mixture to boiling, shaking it, and allowing it to stand. These operations insure the precipitation of chromium, and at least the partial oxidation of iron to the ferric state and its precipitation. The heating and shaking serve also to cause the precipitate to coagulate in flocks, thereby making perceptible a small precipitate, which might otherwise escape detection on account of its transparency.

4. The hydroxide of aluminum is white; that of chromium, grayish-green. The color of the precipitated iron hydroxide varies with the state of oxidation of the iron; pure ferrous salts yielding (if treated with NH_4OH in the absence of ammonium salts) a white precipitate, and ferric salts a dark red one, while mixtures of ferrous and ferric salts give green or black precipitates. In the alkaline mixture the precipitate produced with ferrous salts gradually undergoes corresponding changes in color as a result of progressive oxidation. The precipitate, consisting of $Mn(OH)_3$ and $MnO(OH)_2$, which manganese produces as it becomes oxidized has a dark brown color. With the excess of NH_4OH nickel gives a blue solution, cobalt a purplish-red solution, and chromium (in case it dissolves) a pink solution. Upon oxidation the cobalt solution becomes dark brown. The precipitate produced with a large quantity of cobalt is blue, changing to a bright green on oxidation.

5. The influence of an excess of the NH_4OH and of the presence of ammonium salt on the solubilities of the various hydroxides is explained by the mass-action law and ionic theory as follows: In order that any hydroxide, say of the type $M(OH)_2$, may be precipitated, it is necessary that the product $(M^{++}) \times (OH^-)^2$ of the concentrations of the ions M^{++} and OH^- in the solution under consideration attain the saturation-value of that product. This saturation-value varies, of course, with the nature of the hydroxide; but for all the elements of the aluminum- and iron-groups and for magnesium, it is so small that in a solution containing in 100 cc. only 1 or 2 mg. of the element and a slight excess of NH_4OH, the product $(M^{++}) \times (OH^-)^2$ exceeds it, and precipitation results. When, however, much ammonium salt is also present, this greatly reduces, in virtue of the common-ion effect, the ionization of the NH_4OH and therefore the OH^- concentration in the solution, so that now for certain elements the product $(M^{++}) \times (OH^-)^2$

does not reach the saturation-value, even when (M^{++}) is moderately large (say 500 mg. in 100 cc.). This is true of ferrous iron, manganese, cobalt, and magnesium; but in the cases of the trivalent elements, aluminum, chromium, and ferric iron, the solubility of the hydroxides in water is so slight that even in ammonium salt solutions the solubility is not appreciable.

'If these were the only considerations involved, the greater the excess of NH_4OH added, the less would be the solubility of any hydroxide; but other influences of two kinds come into play with certain of the elements.

The first of these influences is shown by zinc and nickel. In the case of these elements, just as with cadmium and copper, the excess of ammonia combines with the simple cation M^{++}, forming complex cations of the type $M(NH_3)_4^{++}$, thereby removing the simple cation from the solution and making it necessary for more of the hydroxide to dissolve in order to bring back the value of $(M^{++}) \times (OH^-)^2$ to the saturation-value. In such a case the presence of ammonium salt increases the solubility still further, since it greatly decreases the value of (OH^-), owing to the common-ion effect on the ionization of the NH_4OH. Chromium also forms similar ammonia complexes, but in much smaller proportion.

The second kind of influence is exhibited in the case of AlO_3H_3. This hydroxide is, like SnO_2H_2, an example of an amphoteric substance; for it behaves both as a base and as an acid in consequence of its being appreciably ionized both into OH^- and Al^{+++} and into H^+ and $AlO_3H_2^-$ (or into H^+, AlO_2^-, and H_2O). With the H^+ arising from the latter form of ionization the OH^- coming from the excess of NH_4OH combines to form H_2O, so as to satisfy the mass-action expression for the ionization of water, $(H^+) \times (OH^-) =$ a constant (which has the very small value 10^{-14} at $25°$). This causes more AlO_3H_3 to dissolve until the product $(AlO_2^-) \times (H^+)$ again attains its saturation-value. This shows that the quantity of aluminum dissolved increases with the OH^- concentration in the solution, and that therefore it would be much greater in a solution of a largely ionized base like $NaOH$ than in that of a slightly ionized base like NH_4OH. It also shows that the presence of ammonium salts tends to neutralize the solvent action of an excess of NH_4OH, since they decrease the OH^- concentration in its solution.

6. When phosphate is present, magnesium, calcium, strontium, barium, and manganese may be partially, or even completely, precipitated by NH_4OH. The reasons for this are as follows. The normal phosphates and the mono-hydrogen phosphates of these elements are only slightly soluble in water, but dissolve readily in acids, owing to the conversion of the $PO_4^{\equiv}$ and $HPO_4^{=}$ ions into $H_2PO_4^-$ and

(unionized) H_3PO_4 by the H^+ ion of the added acid. Upon the addition of an excess of NH_4OH to such a solution these acid compounds are reconverted into the normal phosphates, and these are reprecipitated. It is therefore necessary, when phosphate is present, to provide for the detection of the alkaline-earth elements in the analysis of the NH_4OH precipitate. They are, however, not necessarily found in that precipitate; for, when other elements, like iron and aluminum, which form much less soluble phosphates, are also present, these may combine with the phosphate-ion present, thus leaving the alkaline-earth elements in solution.

7. There is one other inorganic acidic constituent, namely fluoride, which, like phosphate, may cause the alkaline-earth elements to pass into the NH_4OH precipitate; for barium, strontium, and magnesium fluorides are fairly soluble and calcium fluoride is slightly soluble in dilute HNO_3 without expulsion of the HF (unless the solution is evaporated), and they are much less soluble in dilute NH_4OH solution. It is, however, not important to make special provision for the detection of alkaline-earth elements in the $(NH_4)_2S$ precipitate in the presence of fluoride, since enough barium, strontium, and magnesium remain in solution to be detected by the usual procedure, and since substances containing the slightly soluble CaF_2 are likely to require evaporation with concentrated acids in the Preparation of the Solution (in P. 3 or 5), whereby the fluoride is expelled. Borate also forms with the salts of alkaline-earth elements salts which may require acid for their solution; but these salts are soluble enough so that they are not precipitated from the large volume of hot solution containing ammonium salts to which NH_4OH is added in P. 51. Many organic acidic constituents would cause precipitation of the alkaline-earth elements; but these will have been detected in the closed-tube test (in P. 1) and will have been destroyed in the Preparation of the Solution by the treatment of the substance with HNO_3 and H_2SO_4 (in P. 8). Oxalate is, however, a common organic constituent whose salts do not char much on heating, and one whose presence may cause complete precipitation of calcium and partial precipitation of barium and strontium upon addition of NH_4OH to the acid solution. Provision is therefore made (in P. 65) for the detection of alkaline-earth elements, when the substance is of such a character that it may contain oxalate.

8. $(NH_4)_2S$ precipitates ZnS, MnS, NiS, CoS, and FeS, and converts $Fe(OH)_3$ into Fe_2S_3. The hydroxides of aluminum and chromium are not affected by the $(NH_4)_2S$.

9. The sulfides of iron, nickel, and cobalt are black; ZnS is white; and MnS is flesh-colored, but turns brown on standing in the air, owing to oxidation to $Mn(OH)_3$ and $MnO(OH)_2$.

10. When nickel is present alone or when it forms a large proportion of the $(NH_4)_2S$ precipitate, several milligrams of it usually pass into the filtrate, giving it a brown or black color; and some NiS also passes through the filter with the wash-water. In this case it is useless to try to remove the NiS by filtering again, but it can be coagulated by boiling for several minutes. The brown solution is formed only in the presence of ammonium disulfide, $(NH_4)_2S_2$. Its formation can, as stated above, be avoided by passing H_2S into the NH_4OH solution, instead of adding the $(NH_4)_2S$ reagent, which after exposure to the air always contains some disulfide. The nature of the brown solution is not known.

Procedure 52. — *Separation of the Aluminum-Group from the Iron-Group.* — Transfer the $(NH_4)_2S$ precipitate (P. 51) to a casserole (see Note 1, P. 22), add 5–15 cc. of HCl, stir the mixture for a minute or two in the cold, and then boil it for 1–2 minutes. If there is a black residue, sprinkle into the hot, but not boiling, solution 0.1–0.3 cc. of powdered $KClO_3$, heating nearly to boiling after each addition, till the residue becomes light-colored. Add 5–10 cc. of water, filter out the sulfur residue, and evaporate the filtrate almost to dryness.

Dilute the solution to 10–20 cc., and make it alkaline with NaOH solution (see Note 1, P. 23), adding 10–20 cc. more water if the mixture becomes thick with the precipitate. Place the casserole in a vessel of cold water, and gradually sprinkle into the mixture from a dry 10-cc. graduate 1–3 cc. of Na_2O_2 powder, with constant stirring. (In case phosphate was found present (in P. 50), add also 5 cc. of 3 n. Na_2CO_3 solution.) Boil the mixture for 2–3 minutes, cool it, and dilute it to about 60 cc. (Precipitate, presence of IRON-GROUP.) Filter with the aid of suction, *using a hardened filter;* wash the precipitate thoroughly with hot water, and suck it as dry as possible. (Precipitate, P. 61; filtrate, P. 53.)

Notes. — 1. All the hydroxides and all the sulfides, except NiS and CoS, when freshly precipitated, dissolve readily in cold HCl. If, therefore, there is considerable black residue after adding the HCl, it shows the presence of nickel or cobalt; a very small black residue may, however, be due to FeS enclosed within sulfur. The fact that there is no such dark-colored residue does not, however, prove that nickel and cobalt are entirely absent; for a considerable quantity of them (even 5 mg.) may dissolve completely in the HCl when large quantities of other elements, especially iron, are also present.

2. The $(NH_4)_2S$ precipitate is first treated with HCl, partly in order to furnish the indication just referred to of the presence of nickel or cobalt, but also because much more free sulfur and sulfate would be formed by oxidation if $KClO_3$ (or HNO_3) were used with the HCl at the start. (The formation of sulfate would cause the precipitation of barium if that element was precipitated by NH_4OH because of the presence of phosphate.) If NiS or CoS is present in the residue, $KClO_3$ must, however, be subsequently added, to insure the solution of these sulfides.

3. By NaOH, iron, manganese, nickel, and cobalt are completely precipitated and do not dissolve in moderate excess; while aluminum, chromium, and zinc remain in solution or dissolve when a sufficient excess is added. The solubility of the last three elements is due to the fact that their hydroxides are amphoteric substances which form with the NaOH soluble aluminate $(NaAlO_2)$, chromite $(NaCrO_2)$, and zincate (Na_2ZnO_2), respectively. When zinc and chromium are simultaneously present they are precipitated in the form of zinc chromite, $Zn(CrO_2)_2$. Chromium would also be completely precipitated, owing to hydrolysis of the chromite and the formation of a less soluble solid hydroxide, if the NaOH solution were boiled before adding Na_2O_2. $Mn(OH)_2$ is white, but rapidly turns brown, owing to oxidation to $Mn(OH)_3$; $Ni(OH)_2$ is light green; $Co(OH)_2$ is pink, but from cold cobaltous salt solutions a blue basic salt is first precipitated. If a large excess of NaOH be added, a little $Co(OH)_2$ dissolves, yielding a blue solution, doubtless forming a salt such as Na_2CoO_2. This is to be avoided, since then the cobalt will not be completely oxidized and precipitated upon the subsequent addition of Na_2O_2.

4. By the addition of Na_2O_2, $Fe(OH)_2$ is changed to dark red $Fe(OH)_3$, $Mn(OH)_2$ to brown hydrated MnO_2, and $Co(OH)_2$ to black $Co(OH)_3$, all of which are insoluble in excess of NaOH. Chromium, which after the addition of cold NaOH is present as soluble sodium chromite $(NaCrO_2)$, is converted by Na_2O_2 into chromate (Na_2CrO_4). This remains in solution together with the zinc, which is still present as zincate.

5. Even a cold solution of Na_2O_2 decomposes slowly with evolution of oxygen, and this decomposition takes place with explosive violence when the solution is hot. The peroxide is therefore added in small portions to the cold solution. It is best to transfer a little of it from the can in which it comes in trade directly (without using paper) to a dry 10-cc. graduate, and then to sprinkle it into the solution with

constant stirring. A steady evolution of gas after the mixture has been well stirred is an indication that sufficient peroxide has been added. When much chromium is present, it should be added till the green precipitate disappears and the liquid assumes a dark yellow color. The solution is diluted before filtering in order to avoid the disintegration of the filter-paper. A hardened filter is used, because it is less attacked by strongly alkaline solutions; also because an ordinary filter would disintegrate when treated in P. 61 with 16 n. HNO_3, and by its reducing action prevent the precipitation of manganese. For this last reason an ordinary filter must not under any circumstances be employed for this filtration.

6. This separation with NaOH, Na_2O_2, and Na_2CO_3 is a very satisfactory one, except in the case of zinc. As much as 5 mg. of this element is almost completely carried down in the precipitate when much iron, nickel, or cobalt is present; and as much as 20 mg. of it may be completely precipitated when much manganese is present. Provision is therefore made (in P. 65–66) for the detection of zinc in the precipitate.

7. The Na_2CO_3 is added to insure the complete precipitation of magnesium, calcium, strontium, and barium, whose hydroxides, especially that of barium, are somewhat soluble even in the presence of NaOH. $ZnCO_3$, though insoluble in a dilute solution of Na_2CO_3 alone, dissolves when much NaOH is present, owing to nearly complete conversion of the zinc-ion into zincate-ion ($ZnO_2^=$). The Na_2CO_3 also serves to metathesize barium and strontium chromates, which would otherwise carry chromium into the precipitate and prevent its detection (in P. 57). The Na_2CO_3 solution is added only when phosphate has been detected in P. 50, since its addition is superfluous when alkaline-earth elements cannot be present in the NaOH solution.

8. Phosphate, if present, divides itself in this procedure between the precipitate and solution in a proportion which depends on the nature and quantities of the basic elements present. (See Note 6, P. 51.) Its presence does not cause any of the elements to precipitate which would not otherwise do so, in spite of the slight solubility of aluminum and zinc phosphates. This is due to the fact that the cations of these elements (Al^{+++}, Zn^{++}) are present in the NaOH solution only at an extremely small concentration, owing to their conversion by the OH^- into anions (AlO_2^-, $ZnO_2^=$).

H

ANALYSIS OF THE ALUMINUM-GROUP

TABLE VIII. — ANALYSIS OF THE ALUMINUM-GROUP.

Filtrate from the Sodium Hydroxide and Peroxide Treatment:
$NaAlO_2$, Na_2ZnO_2, Na_2CrO_4. *Acidify with HCl, add NH_4OH (P. 53).*

Precipitate: $Al(OH)_3$. *Dissolve in HNO_3, add $Co(NO_3)_2$, evaporate, ignite (P. 54).*	Filtrate: $Zn(NH_3)_4Cl_2$, Na_2CrO_4. *Add Na_2CO_3, boil to expel NH_3 (P. 55).*	
Blue residue: $Co(AlO_2)_2$.	Precipitate: $ZnCO_3xZn(OH)_2$. *Dissolve in HCl, add NH_4OH and $(NH_4)_2S$ (P. 56).*	Filtrate: Na_2CrO_4. *Add HAc and $PbAc_2$ (P. 57).*
	White precipitate: ZnS.	Yellow precipitate: $PbCrO_4$.

Procedure 53. — *Separation of Aluminum from Chromium and Zinc.* — Acidify the alkaline solution (P. 52) by adding HCl, 5 cc. at first and then 2 cc. at a time, cooling after each addition. Add 5 cc. of 3 n. NH_4Cl solution, and NH_4OH till the mixture after shaking smells of it, then 5 cc. more; and heat almost to boiling. (White flocculent precipitate, presence of ALUMINUM.) Filter, and wash the precipitate. (Precipitate, P. 54; filtrate, P. 55.)

Notes. — 1. In acidifying the solution with HCl care must be taken to keep the solution cool and to avoid adding much excess; since otherwise chromium may be reduced from the state of chromate to that of chromic salt. HNO_3 is not used for the acidification, since it commonly contains HNO_2, which would instantly reduce the chromate.

2. If the chromate is reduced by the HCl, or if the chromic salt was incompletely oxidized to chromate in the Na_2O_2 treatment (in P. 52), green $Cr(OH)_3$ will be precipitated by NH_4OH, together with the $Al(OH)_3$.

3. NH_4Cl and a moderate excess of NH_4OH are added so as to keep the zinc in solution, through the formation of the complex $Zn(NH_3)_4^{++}$ ion, in accordance with the principles described in Note 5, P. 51. A large excess of NH_4OH is avoided, since it would dissolve a little $Al(OH)_3$, owing to formation of NH_4AlO_2.

4. A definite excess of HCl (of not more than 2 cc.) is used in neutralizing the alkaline solution, and a measured volume of NH_4Cl solution is added, so that a proper quantity of Na_2CO_3 solution may be used in precipitating zinc in P. 55.

5. Since aluminum and silica are very likely to be present in the NaOH and Na_2O_2 used as reagents, a blank test for these impurities should be made whenever new reagents are employed for the first time, by treating 10 cc. of the NaOH reagent, or 2 g. of Na_2O_2 added to 20 cc. of water, by P. 53, and comparing the NH_4OH precipitate with that obtained in the actual analysis. It is also well at the same time to test for zinc by passing H_2S into the ammoniacal solution. If the NaOH available is found to contain aluminum or silica, an additional quantity (0.5 cc. more) of Na_2O_2 may be used in place of it in P. 52.

Procedure 54. — *Confirmatory Test for Aluminum.* — Dissolve the NH_4OH precipitate (P. 53), or a small quantity of it if it is large, in 5 cc. of 2 n. HNO_3. To the solution add 5–10 cc. of water, 2–15 drops of 0.3 n. $Co(NO_3)_2$ solution, and 3 cc. of NH_4OH; and heat the mixture nearly to boiling. Filter with the aid of suction, and wash the precipitate with water, finally sucking it as dry as possible. Open the filter paper, tear off the portions to which no precipitate adheres, make a small roll of the remainder, wind a platinum wire around it in the form of a spiral, heat the paper in a flame till the carbon is burnt off, and ignite it for a minute or two at a bright red heat. (Blue residue, presence of ALUMINUM.)

Notes. — 1. A confirmatory test for aluminum should always be tried when the NH_4OH precipitate is small; for the precipitation by NH_4OH of an element whose hydroxide is soluble in NaOH is not very characteristic (lead, antimony, tin, and silicon showing a similar behavior). It is especially necessary to guard against mistaking SiO_3H_2 for $Al(OH)_3$; for the former substance, if not entirely removed in the process of preparing the solution, may appear at this point.

2. The confirmatory test with $Co(NO_3)_2$ depends upon the formation of a blue substance, whose formula is not definitely known; but it is doubtless a compound of the two oxides CoO and Al_2O_3, and is probably cobalt aluminate, $Co(AlO_2)_2$. It enables 0.5 mg. Al to be detected, or even 0.2 mg. after a little practice. No other element gives a blue color to the ash. It is essential to have the aluminum present in excess; for otherwise the blue color is obscured by the black oxide of

cobalt. Moreover, when sodium salts are present, the ash fuses together and the test is unsatisfactory. For this reason the first NH₄OH precipitate (P. 53) is not only washed, but it is dissolved, the aluminum is reprecipitated, and the new precipitate is washed, to insure the complete removal of the sodium salts. The ammonium salts that may be retained by the second precipitate do no harm, as they volatilize when the precipitate is ignited.

3. Although soluble in the ammoniacal solution, a portion of the cobalt added is carried down by the $Al(OH)_3$ precipitate by being deposited on the surface of its particles — a phenomenon known as *adsorption*, which is especially pronounced in the case of gelatinous precipitates in contact with alkaline liquids. In this case, it serves in some measure to adjust the quantity of cobalt associated with the aluminum to the size of the precipitate; but care should also be taken to add a number of drops of the $Co(NO_3)_2$ solution roughly proportional to the amount of the precipitate subjected to the test — using the lower limit, 2 drops, when it contains 1–5 mg. of aluminum, and the upper limit, 15 drops, when it contains 50–100 mg. of aluminum.

Procedure 55. — *Detection of Zinc.* — To the NH₄OH solution (P. 53) add 15 cc. of 3 n. Na_2CO_3 solution, and evaporate in a casserole (to 15–20 cc.) till the solution no longer smells of ammonia. (White precipitate, presence of ZINC.) Wash the precipitate. (Precipitate, P. 56; filtrate, P. 57.)

Notes. — 1. The precipitate produced by Na_2CO_3 is a basic zinc carbonate, $ZnCO_3 \cdot xZn(OH)_2$, containing carbonate and hydroxide in proportions that vary with the conditions of the precipitation. Since it becomes compact during the boiling, even a slight precipitate must not be disregarded. Moreover, since there is usually a small white precipitate of silica, coming from the reagents or from action of the alkali on the dishes, the confirmatory test described in P. 56 must be made if any precipitate whatever separates.

2. The solution is evaporated to a small volume in order to decompose the ammonium salts and expel the NH₃ completely; for even the very slightly soluble basic $ZnCO_3$ is dissolved by NH₄OH, owing to the small dissociation of the $Zn(NH_3)_4^{++}$ complex.

3. Enough Na_2CO_3 solution must be added to react with all the ammonium salt present and to furnish about 5 cc. additional to precipitate the zinc. If an excess of 2 cc. of HCl was used in P. 53 in neutralizing the alkaline solution, and if 5 cc. of 3 n. NH₄Cl solution were added as directed, 9 cc. of the Na_2CO_3 solution will be needed to destroy the ammonium salt, and 15 cc. in all will be sufficient.

Procedure 56. — *Confirmatory Test for Zinc.* — Pour through the filter containing the Na_2CO_3 precipitate (P. 55) 10 cc. of 3 n. HCl. Add NH_4OH to the solution till its odor is perceptible, and then 3 cc. more; and heat the mixture nearly to boiling. Filter out any precipitate, and add 0.5–2.0 cc. of 6 n. $(NH_4)_2S$ solution. (White precipitate, presence of ZINC.) If the result is doubtful, treat the precipitate, or a small portion of it if it is large, by P. 67. Reject the filtrate.

Notes. — 1. The excess of NH_4OH is added to redissolve $Zn(OH)_2$, which may separate when a large quantity of zinc is present. The solution is then filtered, unless perfectly clear, to remove any $Al(OH)_3$, $Cr(OH)_3$, or H_2SiO_3 which may still be present.

2. When a white flocculent precipitate or (with a small quantity of zinc) a translucent turbidity is produced by the $(NH_4)_2S$, it is sufficient evidence of the presence of zinc. But, if a darkened precipitate is produced, the presence of zinc in it should be confirmed by P. 67.

Procedure 57. — *Detection of Chromium.* — Acidify the filtrate from the Na_2CO_3 precipitate (P. 55) with HAc, add 20 cc. of water, heat the mixture nearly to boiling, and add 3–15 cc. of $PbAc_2$ solution. (Yellow precipitate, presence of CHROMIUM.)

Note. — The solution is diluted and heated nearly to boiling so as to prevent the precipitation of $PbCl_2$.

ANALYSIS OF THE IRON-GROUP

TABLE IX. — ANALYSIS OF THE IRON-GROUP.

Precipitate Produced by Sodium Hydroxide and Peroxide:

A. Phosphate absent: $MnO(OH)_2$, $Fe(OH)_3$,*$Zn(OH)_2$, $Co(OH)_3$, $Ni(OH)_2$.

B. Phosphate present: Also $FePO_4$, and alkaline-earth phosphates and carbonates.

Heat with HNO_3 and $KClO_3$ (P. 61).

Precipitate: MnO_2. *Add HNO_3 and H_2O_2 (P. 62).*	Solution: *A.* $Fe(NO_3)_3$, $Zn(NO_3)_2$, $Co(NO_3)_2$, $Ni(NO_3)_2$. *Add NH_4OH (P. 63).* *B.* Also $Ba(NO_3)_2$, etc., and H_3PO_4. *Nearly neutralize with NH_4OH, add NH_4Ac and $Fe(NO_3)_3$, dilute, and boil (P. 64).*†		
Solution: $Mn(NO_3)_2$. *Add BiO_2*	Precipitate: *A.* $Fe(OH)_3$. *B.* Also $FePO_4$.	Filtrate. *Add NH_4OH, pass in H_2S (P. 65).*	
Purple color: $HMnO_4$.		Precipitate: ZnS, CoS, NiS. See Table X.	Filtrate: *A.* NH_4 salts. *Reject.* *B.* Ba, Ca, Sr, Mg, and NH_4 salts. *Treat by P. 71.*

* All the zinc may be carried into this precipitate by elements of the iron-group when they are present in large quantity.

† First testing a small portion of the solution for iron with $K_4Fe(CN)_6$.

Procedure 61. — *Precipitation of Manganese.* — Transfer the Na_2O_2 precipitate (P. 52) to a wide-mouth 50 cc. conical flask, and add 5–10 cc. of 16 n. HNO_3. Remove the filter-paper with a glass rod, but do not filter out any undissolved residue. Place the flask in a beaker of boiling water, add gradually 0.5 cc. of powdered $KClO_3$, and continue to heat the mixture for 1–2 minutes. (Black precipitate, presence of MANGANESE.)

In case there is no precipitate, treat the solution by P. 63 if in P. 50 phosphate was found absent, or by P. 64 if phosphate was found present.

In case there is a precipitate, add gradually powdered $KClO_3$, 0.5 cc. at a time, heating (in the water-bath) for 1–2 minutes after each addition, till no further precipitation takes place, not adding more than 3 cc. in any case. Filter the mixture with the aid of suction through an asbestos filter made by placing in a funnel a 2 cm. perforated plate (or enough glass-wool to form a wad 1 cm. high, tamping it down with the finger), and pouring through it enough of a suspension of fine asbestos fibers in water to form a layer of asbestos about 3 mm. thick, applying suction at the same time. Collect the filtrate in a test-tube placed within the filter-bottle. Wash the precipitate with a little water, and treat it by P. 62. Treat the filtrate by P. 63 if in P. 50 phosphate was found absent, or by P. 64 if phosphate was found present.

Notes. — 1. The treatment with 16 n. HNO_3 dissolves all the substances that may be present in the Na_2O_2 precipitate except $MnO(OH)_2$; and this may be dissolved wholly or in part by the nitrous acid that is present in the HNO_3 or is produced by the action of it on the filter-paper. Any residue of $MnO(OH)_2$ is not filtered off or brought into solution, since the manganese is to be immediately precipitated as MnO_2.

2. By $HClO_3$ in hot HNO_3 solution (but not by HNO_3 alone) manganous salts are rapidly oxidized to MnO_2 with formation of ClO_2 (chlorine dioxide), which escapes as a yellow gas.

3. The $KClO_3$ is added gradually, so as to avoid too violent action in case much manganese is present, or the use of an unnecessary excess in case only a little manganese is present. The mixture is heated in a water-bath, instead of directly over a flame, in order to avoid the risk of the acid being thrown out of the flask by bumping, and in order to obviate the danger of an explosion, which might occur if a large quantity of ClO_2 vapor were suddenly produced and exposed to a temperature above 100°. Although ClO_2 is highly explosive, having a great tendency to decompose into its elements, no danger is involved in this Procedure (where the mixture is heated in a water-bath) provided a large quantity of $KClO_3$ be not added at one time.

4. The separation of manganese in this way from the other metals of this group is entirely satisfactory with the exception that a small quantity of iron (up to 1 mg.) may be completely carried down with a large quantity (500 mg.) of manganese.

Procedure 62. — *Confirmatory Test for Manganese.* — Pour through the filter containing the $HClO_3$ precipitate (**P. 61**)

(handwritten at top: H_2O_2 first - Potass. dichromate + H_2SO_4 + ether + H_2O_2 blue ring.)

5 cc. of hot HNO_3 to which 10 drops of 3% H_2O_2 solution have been added. Collect the filtrate in a test-tube; cool it; add to it solid bismuth dioxide, 0.1 cc. at a time, till a purple color results, or till some of the brown solid remains undissolved; and let the solid settle. (Purple solution, presence of MANGANESE.)

> *Notes.* — 1. This confirmatory test for manganese is usually superfluous, since the precipitation of manganese by $HClO_3$ is highly characteristic.
>
> 2. An excess of bismuth dioxide must be added, since otherwise the manganese may be oxidized only to MnO_2.
>
> 3. Commercial bismuth dioxide, also often called sodium bismuthate, is a mixture of bismuth compounds which probably owes its oxidizing power to the presence of the dioxide BiO_2. When it is not available, PbO_2 may be substituted for it; but in that case the mixture must be boiled for 2 or 3 minutes.

Procedure 63. — *Precipitation of Iron in the Absence of Phosphate.* — In case phosphate is absent, pour the cold HNO_3 solution (P. 61), all at once, into a volume of 6 n. NH_4OH four times as large as that of the 16 n. HNO_3 used in P. 61. (Dark red precipitate, presence of IRON.) Filter, and wash the precipitate. Treat the filtrate by P. 65. Pour on to the filter containing the precipitate 2 cc. of $K_4Fe(CN)_6$ solution to which 10 drops of HAc have been added. (Dark blue or green residue, presence of IRON.)

> *Notes.* — 1. The HNO_3 solution is poured all at once into a large excess of NH_4OH; for, unless the iron is precipitated very rapidly from a solution containing a large quantity of ammonium salts and ammonia, it may carry down with it nearly all the cobalt and nickel, when a small quantity is present. Thus, if the precipitation is made in the usual way by adding NH_4OH, a little at a time, to a diluted HNO_3 solution, 10 mg. or more of cobalt and 2–3 mg. of nickel are carried down by 500 mg. of iron so completely that these elements can hardly be detected in the subsequent Procedures; while with the process described in this Procedure 10–20% of the cobalt and about 50% of the nickel pass into the filtrate when small quantities of them are present with 250–500 mg. of iron.
>
> 2. By treatment with $K_4Fe(CN)_6$ the $Fe(OH)_3$ is converted into ferric ferrocyanide (Prussian blue), provided some HAc be present so that the hydroxide may be slightly dissolved.

Procedure 64. — *Precipitation of Iron and Phosphate in Presence of Phosphate.* — Evaporate one-tenth of the HNO₃ solution (P. 61) almost to dryness, heat the residue with 3 cc. of HCl till the odor of chlorine disappears, and add about 20 cc. of water and 3–30 drops of $K_4Fe(CN)_6$ solution. (Dark blue precipitate, presence of IRON.)

Neutralize the remainder of the HNO₃ solution with NH₄OH, adding it toward the end 15 drops at a time till a precipitate forms which fails to redissolve after shaking the mixture for 10–15 seconds (or till it becomes alkaline in case there is no precipitate, in which case treat the mixture directly by P. 65). Then add 50 cc. of water and 15 cc. of 3 n. NH₄Ac solution. Add also, unless the mixture is already reddish in color, $Fe(NO_3)_3$ solution, 1 cc. at a time, till such a color is produced. Boil the mixture gently for 2–3 minutes, adding 30–50 cc. more water if a large precipitate separates. (If the iron does not precipitate, but remains in the colloidal state, add 10–30 drops more of NH₄OH and boil again.) Filter while still hot, with the aid of suction. Reject the precipitate. Make the filtrate alkaline with NH₄OH; filter out any precipitate, and treat the filtrate by P. 65.

Notes. — 1. This separation of ferric iron from the bivalent elements depends on the facts that, upon boiling an acetic acid solution containing much acetate, the iron is completely precipitated as $Fe(OH)_3$ and $Fe(OH)_2Ac$ (basic ferric acetate); and that all the phosphate present combines with the iron when it is present in excess, and therefore then passes completely into the precipitate, leaving the bivalent elements in solution.

2. The precipitation of the iron takes place in virtue of the hydrolysis (that is, the decomposition by water) of the ferric acetate into HAc and $Fe(OH)_3$ or $Fe(OH)_2Ac$. The formation of $Fe(OH)_3$ may be expressed by the equation:

$$Fe^{+++} + 3\ Ac^- + 3\ HOH = 3\ HAc + Fe(OH)_3.$$

The concentration of $Fe(OH)_3$ evidently tends, in accordance with the mass-action law, to become greater (thereby insuring its more complete precipitation), the less the concentration of the (unionized) HAc and the greater the concentration of Ac^- ion. For this reason the HNO₃ in the solution is carefully neutralized almost completely, and a large quantity of NH₄Ac is added. Some free HAc must, however, be left in the solution and an undue excess of NH₄Ac must not be present, since otherwise the hydroxides of the bivalent elements of the iron-group would precipitate with the iron. The $Fe(OH)_3$ formed by the hydrolysis tends to remain in solution in the colloidal state. Its coagulation is greatly promoted by the boiling of the solution.

3. The precipitation of the phosphate in combination with the iron, rather than with the alkaline-earth elements, depends on the fact that the solubility of $FePO_4$ in water (and therefore also in HAc) is much smaller than that of the phosphates of the bivalent elements. The ion-concentration product of the $FePO_4$ therefore attains its saturation-value and removes the PO_4 from the solution long before the ion-concentration product of the bivalent phosphate attains its saturation-value.

4. In order, however, that the alkaline-earth phosphates may not be precipitated from the very weak HAc solution, more than enough iron must be present to combine with all the phosphate in the solution. If this amount of iron is already present, the mixture after addition of the NH₄Ac will have a reddish color, since $FeAc_3$ in cold solution has a deep red color. If this amount is not present, the mixture will be colorless or light yellow (unless cobalt or nickel is present), since even if there is some iron in the solution, it will be converted into $FePO_4$ which forms a yellowish white precipitate. In this case, $Fe(NO_3)_3$ is added till the mixture becomes reddish.

Procedure 65. — *Precipitation of Zinc, Cobalt, and Nickel.* — Into the ammoniacal solution (P. 63 or 64) pass a moderate current of H_2S for about a minute at a time, till, after thorough shaking, the vapors above the mixture darken PbAc₂ paper. (White precipitate, presence of ZINC; black precipitate or coloration, presence of NICKEL or COBALT; no darkening of the mixture, absence of NICKEL and COBALT.) Filter, and wash the precipitate with water containing 1% of 6 n. (NH₄)₂S solution. (In case the filtrate is dark colored, boil it till the dark color disappears, and filter out and wash any precipitate, uniting it, if dark-colored, with that previously obtained.) Treat the precipitate by P. 67 in case it is white, or by P. 66 in case it is dark-colored. Treat the filtrate by P. 71–79 in case phosphate was found present in P. 50, or in case the original substance may have contained oxalate (see Note 4); treat the filtrate by

P. 78–79 in case chromium was found present in **P.** 57; otherwise, reject the filtrate.

Notes. — 1. In this precipitation H_2S is used instead of $(NH_4)_2S$, since with the latter reagent much of the nickel may remain unprecipitated, yielding a brown solution. Even with H_2S a little nickel may pass into the filtrate, especially if a large excess of H_2S is not avoided by shaking the mixture and testing the vapors above it with $PbAc_2$ paper at frequent intervals.

2. Since not more than 20 mg. of zinc can be present in the ammoniacal solution (see Note 6, P. 52), and since 1 mg. of nickel or cobalt causes a pronounced darkening of such a small quantity of ZnS, it is safe to conclude that nickel and cobalt are absent when no such darkening occurs, and the further Procedures for detecting these elements (P. 66 and 68) may be omitted.

3. The filtrate must be tested for alkaline-earth elements (by P. 71–79) in case phosphate was found present (in P. 50), or in case the original substance may have contained oxalate; for these elements may then be found wholly or in large part in this filtrate, as explained in Notes 6 and 7, P. 51, and Note 1, P. 64. Since the filtrate contains sodium salts, it must not be united with that from the original $(NH_4)_2S$ precipitate (obtained in P. 51), but must be separately treated by P. 71–79.

4. Oxalate, like other organic acidic constituents, is never present in minerals or alloys, nor in industrial products which have been subjected to a high temperature. It may, however, be present in other industrial products; therefore, when the original substance is of a character and from a source that makes possible the presence of oxalate, the filtrate obtained in the Procedure should be tested for alkaline-earth elements. These elements will not be reprecipitated by NH_4OH in P. 63 or 64, but will pass into the ammoniacal filtrate, since the oxalic acid is oxidized to CO_2 and H_2O by the $HClO_3$ used in P. 61.

5. The filtrate is tested for magnesium when chromium was found present in P. 57, since any magnesium present may then have been completely carried down with it in the $(NH_4)_2S$ precipitate, as stated in Note 2, P. 51.

TABLE X. — SEPARATION OF ZINC, COBALT, AND NICKEL.

Hydrogen Sulphide Precipitate: ZnS, CoS, NiS.
Treat with cold 1 n. HCl (P. 66).

| Solution: $ZnCl_2$, $CoCl_2$*, $NiCl_2$*. Add NaOH and Na_2O_2 (P. 66). | Residue: CoS, NiS. |

| Filtrate: Na_2ZnO_2. *Add $(NH_4)_2S$.* | Precipitate: $Co(OH)_3$, $Ni(OH)_2$. |

Add HCl and $KClO_3$ (P. 68).

| White precipitate: ZnS. *Dissolve in HNO_3, add $Co(NO_3)_2$ and Na_2CO_3, ignite (P. 67).* | Solution: $CoCl_2$, $NiCl_2$. *Evaporate, add HAc and KNO_2 (P. 68).* |

| Green residue: $CoZnO_2$. | Yellow precipitate: $K_3Co(NO_2)_6$. | Filtrate: $NiCl_2$. *Add $(CH_3)_2C_2(NOH)_2$.* |

| | | Red precipitate: $[(CH_3)_2C_2(NOH)NO]_2Ni$. |

---

* A small proportion of the cobalt and nickel present always dissolves in the dilute HCl.

Procedure 66. — *Separation of Zinc from Cobalt and Nickel.* — Transfer the H_2S precipitate (P. 65) in case it was at all darkened, to a casserole. Add 10–30 cc. of 1 n. HCl, stir the (cold) mixture frequently for 5 minutes, and filter it. (Black residue, presence of COBALT or NICKEL.) Wash the residue and treat it by P. 68 (after uniting it with the Na_2O_2 precipitate obtained from the filtrate). Boil the filtrate till the H_2S is completely expelled, make the mixture alkaline with NaOH solution, cool it, and add gradually 0.5–1.0 cc. of Na_2O_2 powder. Boil the mixture gently for 2–3 minutes, cool it, and filter it. (Black precipitate, presence of COBALT; green precipitate, presence of NICKEL.) Wash the precipitate, unite it with the residue undissolved by dilute HCl, and treat the mixture by P. 68. To the filtrate add 3–10 drops of 6 n. $(NH_4)_2S$ solution. (White precipitate, presence of ZINC.) Filter out and wash the precipitate, and treat it by P. 67.

Notes. — 1. This treatment with 1 n. HCl serves to extract from the cobalt and nickel sulfides nearly all the zinc which may be present in this precipitate because of its having been carried down in the Na_2O_2 precipitate, as described in Note 6, P. 52. A small proportion of the cobalt and nickel present (5–20%) always dissolves in the 1n. HCl, and the subsequent treatment with Na_2O_2 serves to separate these elements from the zinc. This Na_2O_2 separation is satisfactory when, as in this HCl solution, the cobalt and nickel are present in small quantity; for then only an insignificant amount of zinc is carried down with them.

2. This Procedure must always be followed in order to determine whether or not zinc is present in the substance, unless a satisfactory test for it has already been obtained in P. 56, or unless the original Na_2O_2 precipitate (P. 52) was small. In either of these two cases this Procedure may be omitted and the H_2S precipitate (P. 65) treated directly by P. 68.

3. The fact that CoS and NiS do not dissolve readily in 1 n. HCl seems inconsistent with the non-precipitation of cobalt and nickel by H_2S with the copper- and tin-groups from a solution which is only 0.3 normal in acid. This behavior probably arises from the fact that these sulfides exist in at least two allotropic forms of different solubilities. The form that is first produced when sulfide-ion is brought together with nickel-ion or cobalt-ion is soluble in dilute acid; but this form changes on standing or heating into a less soluble form, which is not produced directly except when the ion-constituents are mixed at fairly high concentrations. This would explain also the fact that the CoS and NiS precipitated by $(NH_4)_2S$ dissolve partly, but not wholly, in dilute HCl; for there are doubtless present in these precipitates both the more soluble and the less soluble forms — the latter in larger proportion the longer the precipitates have been heated and the longer they have stood.

4. NaOH precipitates cobalt as blue CoCl(OH), changing to pink $Co(OH)_2$, and nickel as light-green $Ni(OH)_2$. By the addition of Na_2O_2, the cobalt is oxidized to black $Co(OH)_3$, and its precipitation made more complete.

5. Only a small quantity (0.5–1.0 cc.) of Na_2O_2 powder is added, since the quantity of cobalt and nickel dissolved by the dilute HCl never exceeds 100 mg. The solution is subsequently boiled to decompose the excess of Na_2O_2, since otherwise it would destroy the $(NH_4)_2S$ added to precipitate the zinc.

Procedure 67. — *Confirmatory Test for Zinc.* — Dissolve the H_2S precipitate (P. 65) in case it was white, or the $(NH_4)_2S$ precipitate (P. 67), by pouring a 5–10 cc. portion of HNO_3 repeatedly through the filter. To the solution add from a dropper 1–3 drops of 0.3 n. $Co(NO_3)_2$ solution. Evaporate the mixture just to dryness, and add 1–3 cc. of 3 n. Na_2CO_3 solution. Evaporate again to dryness, and ignite the residue at a low temperature by keeping the dish moving to and fro in a small flame till the purple color due to the cobalt disappears; let the casserole cool, and moisten the residue with water. (Green residue, presence of ZINC.) (If the ignited mass becomes black, owing to too strong heating, add a few drops of HNO_3, evaporate just to dryness, add the same quantity of Na_2CO_3 solution as was added before, evaporate and ignite as before.)

Notes. — 1. This confirmatory test is useful when there results only a small noncoagulating precipitate which may be sulfur, or when, owing to the presence of a small quantity of other elements, the precipitate is dark-colored.

2. In this test the use of an excess of $Co(NO_3)_2$ is avoided, since otherwise the black color of the CoO obscures the green color of the cobalt zincate ($CoZnO_2$); and for this reason the amount of $Co(NO_3)_2$ added is adjusted within the limits stated to the quantity of the precipitate tested. The test when properly made will detect 0.5 mg. or less of zinc.

Procedure 68. — *Detection of Cobalt and Nickel.* — Dissolve the residue from the HCl treatment and the Na_2O_2 precipitate (P. 66) in a casserole by adding 5–15 cc. of HCl, heating the mixture nearly to boiling, and sprinkling into it 0.1–0.3 cc. of powdered $KClO_3$. Filter out any sulfur residue, and evaporate the solution just to dryness. Dissolve the residue in 5 cc. of HAc. To the solution in a test-tube add 3 cc. of 6 n. KNO_2 solution, and let the mixture stand with occasional shaking for at least 15 minutes. (Yellow precipitate, presence of COBALT.) If a considerable precipitate forms, add to the mixture 10 cc. more of 6 n. KNO_2 solution and 4 cc. of powdered KCl, and let it stand with frequent shaking for at least 15 minutes. Filter. Reject the precipitate. To one-fourth of the filtrate add 10 cc.

of water and 4 cc. of a 0.1 n. dimethylglyoxime solution in ethylalcohol, heat the mixture nearly to boiling, and let it stand 5–10 minutes. (Red precipitate, presence of NICKEL.) Reject the remainder of the filtrate.

Notes. — 1. Only a small quantity (3 cc.) of KNO_2 solution is added at first, since in the small volume of solution this suffices to give a distinct precipitate with less than 1 mg. of cobalt within 15 minutes, and since with this small quantity there is no danger that nickel will be precipitated. In case a considerable precipitate forms, a much larger quantity of the KNO_2 reagent is added, together with enough solid KCl to nearly saturate the solution, in order to precipitate nearly all of the cobalt; for the presence of much cobalt interferes with the subsequent test for nickel. Even though under these conditions some nickel may be precipitated, especially when much of it is present together with a large quantity of cobalt, only a small proportion of the nickel present is ever carried down.

2. The principles involved in this separation of cobalt from nickel are as follows. A small proportion of the cobalt present is oxidized by the HNO_2 from the cobaltous to the cobaltic state (from the state of Co^{++} to Co^{+++} ions). The value of the reduction-potential for Co^{++}, Co^{+++}, is, however, such that the oxidation must soon cease unless the Co^{+++} ions are removed from the solution. This is effected in this case by the KNO_2 through the conversion of the Co^{+++} ions into the complex anion $Co(NO_2)_6^{\equiv}$ and through the precipitation of the latter in the form of the slightly soluble $K_3Co(NO_2)_6$ (potassium cobaltinitrite). It is clear from these statements that, in accordance with the mass-action law, a large concentration of HNO_2 will hasten the oxidation of the cobaltous ion, that a large concentration of NO_2^- ion will cause more complete conversion of the cobaltic ion into the cobaltinitrite ion, and that a large concentration of K^+ ion will diminish the solubility of the potassium cobaltinitrite. It will be seen that all these conditions are provided for in the Procedure. The nickel is not appreciably oxidized by HNO_2 to the nickelic state. When it is precipitated by KNO_2, it is in the form of the (fairly soluble) potassium nickelous nitrite $K_4Ni(NO_2)_6$.

3. Only one-fourth of the filtrate is used for the nickel test with dimethylglyoxime, since this suffices to give the desired delicacy, since it enables the quantity of nickel present to be better estimated, and since it diminishes the quantity of cobalt present in the solution tested. It is desirable that not much cobalt be present, since a smaller volume of the (rather expensive) reagent is then required; for a quantity of

the dimethylglyoxime equivalent to the cobalt present must be added before a small quantity of nickel will yield a precipitate. This is probably due to the fact that the cobalt combines with the reagent forming a soluble complex salt.

4. Dimethylglyoxime is a weak monobasic organic acid of the composition $(CH_3)_2C_2(NOH)_2$. The brilliant red substance is its nickel salt, formed by replacing by one nickel atom one hydrogen atom in each of two dimethylglyoxime molecules. The precipitate is so slightly soluble, so voluminous, and so highly colored that less than 0.1 mg. of nickel can be detected in the solution tested.

PRECIPITATION AND ANALYSIS OF THE ALKALINE-EARTH GROUP

TABLE XI. — ANALYSIS OF THE ALKALINE-EARTH GROUP.

Ammonium Carbonate Precipitate:
$BaCO_3$, $SrCO_3$, $CaCO_3$, $MgCO_3 \cdot (NH_4)_2CO_3$.
Dissolve in HAc, add NH_4Ac and K_2CrO_4 (P. 72).

Precipitate: $BaCrO_4$.	Filtrate. *Add NH_4OH and C_2H_5OH (P. 74).*			
Dissolve in HCl, evaporate, add HAc, NH_4Ac, and K_2CrO_4 (P. 73).	Precipitate: $SrCrO_4$, $(CaCrO_4)$.* *Boil with $(NH_4)_2CO_3$ and $K_2C_2O_4$, (P. 75).*		Filtrate: Ca and Mg salts. *Add $K_2C_2O_4$ (P. 76).*	
	Residue: $SrCO_3$, (CaC_2O_4). *Treat with HAc.*		Precipitate: CaC_2O_4, (MgC_2O_4). *Treat with H_2SO_4.*	Filtrate. *Add Na_2HPO_4 (P. 78).*
Precipitate: $BaCrO_4$.				
	Solution: $SrAc_2$. *Add Na_2SO_4.*	Residue: (CaC_2O_4).	Solution: $CaSO_4$, $(MgSO_4)$. *Add C_2H_5OH (P. 77).*	Precipitate: $MgNH_4PO_4$.
	Precipitate: $SrSO_4$.		Precipitate: $CaSO_4$.	

* Substances whose formulas are within parentheses are not normally found at the point indicated, but their presence (arising from faulty procedure or an excessive proportion of the element in the substance) is provided for in the confirmatory tests.

Procedure 71. — *Precipitation of the Alkaline-Earth Group.* — Evaporate the filtrate from the $(NH_4)_2S$ precipitate (P. 51) till salts crystallize out, dilute it to a volume of 10 cc., cool it, and filter out any sulphur or crystalline salts that have separated.

To the filtrate add 15 cc. of 6 n. $(NH_4)_2CO_3$ solution and 15 cc. of 95% C_2H_5OH (ethyl alcohol); and, if a large precipitate results, add 15 cc. more of each of these liquids. Shake the mixture continuously for 10 minutes; or better, let it stand, with frequent shaking, for at least half an hour. (Precipitate, presence of ALKALINE-EARTH ELEMENTS.) Filter, and wash the precipitate with a little $(NH_4)_2CO_3$ reagent, using suction if

I

the precipitate is large. Treat the precipitate by P. 72. Treat the filtrate by P. 81 or P. 85 (see the General Discussion of the Alkali-Group on page 121).

Notes. — 1. The filtrate from the $(NH_4)_2S$ precipitate is evaporated in order that the elements of the alkaline-earth group may be precipitated more quickly and more completely. The evaporation also serves to destroy $(NH_4)_2S$ and to coagulate any sulfur that may separate. The volume to which the $(NH_4)_2CO_3$ reagent is added should be 10 cc.

2. If the ammonium carbonate solution were added in only small excess, the precipitation of $CaCO_3$, $SrCO_3$, and $BaCO_3$ would not be complete, and additional tests for small quantities of these elements would have to be made in the filtrate. But, by the use of a large quantity of a concentrated solution of $(NH_4)_2CO_3$ containing NH_4OH (so as to diminish the hydrolysis of the carbonate into $(NH_4)^+HCO_3^-$ and NH_4OH), the precipitation may be made practically complete, owing to the large concentration of carbonate-ion $(CO_3^=)$.

3. By making, as in the Procedure, the concentration of the $(NH_4)_2CO_3$ sufficiently great, magnesium is in the cold also completely precipitated. The precipitate, which is in this case a double carbonate, $MgCO_3 \cdot (NH_4)_2CO_3 \cdot 4 H_2O$, is, however, fairly soluble in cold water and readily soluble in hot water.

4. From a cold aqueous solution the precipitation of these elements takes place slowly, especially in the case of magnesium and calcium; but it is greatly accelerated by the addition of alcohol and by shaking. Under the conditions recommended in the procedure 0.5 mg. of any of the four elements gives a precipitate.

Procedure 72. — *Precipitation of Barium.* — Pour repeatedly through the filter containing the $(NH_4)_2CO_3$ precipitate (P. 71) a 5–15 cc. portion of hot HAc, and evaporate the solution just to dryness, taking care not to ignite the residue.

Add to the residue 2 cc. of HAc, 10 cc. of 3 n. NH_4Ac solution, and 10 cc. of water, and heat the mixture nearly to boiling in a flask. Add just 3 cc. of 3 n. K_2CrO_4 solution, 5 drops at a time, shaking after each addition, and heat the mixture nearly to boiling for 5 minutes, with frequent shaking. (Yellow precipitate, presence of BARIUM.) In case a considerable precipitate forms, add 2 cc. more of the K_2CrO_4 solution, and heat and shake the mixture. Filter, even though the solution appear clear. (Precipitate P. 73; filtrate P. 74.)

Notes. — 1. The separation of the first three elements of this group depends on the difference in the solubilities of their chromates. These solubilities increase rapidly in the order, Ba, Sr, Ca, as shown in the Table in the Appendix. The difference in the solubilities of $BaCrO_4$ and $SrCrO_4$ is so great that under the conditions of the procedure 0.5 mg. Ba can be detected, while 500 mg. of strontium give no precipitate, even when 5 cc. of K_2CrO_4 solution have been added.

2. In case a large quantity of barium is present, a second portion of the K_2CrO_4 reagent is added; for though the quantity of K_2CrO_4 present in the 3 cc. first added is equivalent to about 600 mg. of barium, yet the excess left in the solution when much barium is present may be so small as not to precipitate it completely. A larger amount of K_2CrO_4 is not added at first, and it is not added at all unless the presence of much barium makes it necessary, since it would increase the tendency of strontium (and in P. 74 of calcium) to precipitate.

3. Acetic acid is added to increase the solubility of $SrCrO_4$. By its action the concentration of the chromate-ion is decreased, owing to its conversion partly into hydrochromate-ion and partly into bichromate-ion, according to the reactions:

$$CrO_4^= + H^+ = HCrO_4^-; \text{ and } 2\,HCrO_4^- = H_2O + Cr_2O_7^=.$$

It is evident that the ratio of the $CrO_4^=$ to the $HCrO_4^-$ concentration must decrease as the H^+ concentration increases. For this reason the presence of a largely ionized acid (such as HCl or HNO_3) would prevent the complete precipitation of $BaCrO_4$; but since HAc is only a slightly ionized acid, and since a large amount of acetate is present, the addition of a considerable quantity of HAc has only a slight effect on the solubility.

4. The K_2CrO_4 is added slowly to the hot solution and the mixture is shaken and heated in the neighborhood of 100° before filtering, since otherwise the precipitate is liable to pass through the filter.

5. By adding the reagent gradually almost all the barium is precipitated before an excess of K_2CrO_4 is present. This is of importance, since, when much barium is present, even 3 mg. of strontium may be carried down completely if the K_2CrO_4 reagent be added quickly.

6. When less than 1 mg. of barium is present, it is difficult to distinguish the faint turbidity in the colored solution. It is therefore directed to filter the mixture even when it appears clear; for a very small yellow precipitate can be seen on the filter after washing out the K_2CrO_4 solution.

Procedure 73. — *Confirmatory Test for Barium.* — In case in P. 74 much strontium is found present, pour repeatedly through the filter containing the K_2CrO_4 precipitate (P. 73) a 5–10 cc. portion of hot HCl, and evaporate the solution just to dryness. Treat the residue as described in the second paragraph of P. 72, using however only one-half of the prescribed volume of each of the reagents. (Yellow precipitate, presence of BARIUM.)

Note. — In case a large quantity of strontium is present, as shown by the formation of a large precipitate in P. 74, some of it may be precipitated by K_2CrO_4 in P. 72, especially if the directions as to the quantities of the reagents have not been followed. The strontium will not, however, again precipitate in this second treatment; for the quantity of it now present in the solution is much less than before. A yellow precipitate now obtained is therefore conclusive evidence of the presence of barium.

Procedure 74. — *Precipitation of Strontium.* — To the filtrate from the K_2CrO_4 precipitate (P. 72) add NH_4OH slowly till the color changes from orange to yellow, and then 5 cc. more. Heat the solution to 60–70°, and add to it 15 cc. of 95% C_2H_5OH 5 cc. at a time, shaking for 10–15 seconds after each addition if a precipitate forms. Cool the solution in running water, shaking it continuously; and let the mixture stand at least 5 minutes. (Light yellow precipitate, presence of STRONTIUM.) In case considerable precipitate forms, add 5 cc. of 3 n. K_2CrO_4 solution and 15 cc. of 95% C_2H_5OH, shake the mixture and let it stand at least 5 minutes. Filter with the aid of suction (see Note 4); suck the precipitate as dry as possible, but do not wash it. (Precipitate, P. 75; filtrate, P. 76.)

Notes. — 1. Under these conditions 1 mg. of strontium yields a precipitate, and 500 mg. of calcium or magnesium do not do so, provided not more than 3 cc. of K_2CrO_4 solution and 15 cc. of C_2H_5OH have been added. Upon the addition of the second portions of these reagents, a precipitate of $CaCrO_4$ may separate when a large quantity of calcium is present. This does not interfere with the detection of strontium; for these additional amounts of reagent are added, in order to precipitate completely a large quantity of strontium, only when the smaller amounts have already produced a considerable precipitate.

2. Since calcium may precipitate even at first if the concentrations of the reagents differ much from those prescribed, the confirmatory test for strontium should always be tried.

3. The alcohol is added to the hot solution, in small portions, and with vigorous shaking, so that all the $SrCrO_4$ may not be suddenly precipitated, which may cause it to separate in so fine a form that it passes through the pores of the filter-paper.

4. If the filtrate is not perfectly clear, even after a second filtration, it may be made so by adding some paper-pulp, shaking vigorously for a minute or two, and again filtering with the aid of suction. The pulp may be made by shaking violently a filter-paper torn into small pieces with 10 cc. of water in a stoppered test-tube, and pressing out most of the water between the fingers.

5. The precipitate is not washed, since $SrCrO_4$ is fairly soluble in water.

Procedure 75. — *Confirmatory Test for Strontium.* — Pour repeatedly through the filter containing the K_2CrO_4 precipitate (P.74) a 10-cc. portion of boiling water. Add to the solution just 1 cc. of 3 n. Na_2CO_3 solution and 12 cc. of 3 n. $K_2C_2O_4$ solution, and boil the mixture gently in a covered casserole for 5 minutes. Filter the boiling mixture. Reject the filtrate. Wash the precipitate thoroughly with water, and pour repeatedly through the filter 5 cc. of cold 1 n. HAc. To the solution add 2 cc. of Na_2SO_4 solution, heat the mixture to boiling, and let it stand 10 minutes. (White precipitate, presence of STRONTIUM.)

Notes. — 1. In a boiling solution containing oxalate and carbonate in the proportions recommended in the Procedure small quantities of strontium and calcium are converted in a few minutes almost completely into $SrCO_3$ and CaC_2O_4, respectively. This behavior arises from the facts that in the hot mixture $SrCO_3$ is less soluble than SrC_2O_4, while CaC_2O_4 is less soluble than $CaCO_3$.

2. The mixture is filtered while still near the boiling temperature; for in the cold the solubility relations are such that SrC_2O_4 instead of $SrCO_3$ results.

3. $SrCO_3$ is readily dissolved by 1 n. HAc, but CaC_2O_4 is only slightly dissolved by this acid. Any small quantity of calcium that passes into solution would not give a precipitate with Na_2SO_4, since $CaSO_4$ is a moderately soluble salt.

4. Of any barium that may be contained in the K_2CrO_4 precipitate only enough is dissolved by the boiling water (in the presence of the K_2CrO_4 and NH_4OH remaining in the filter-paper) to give a scarcely noticeable turbidity with the Na_2SO_4 solution.

Procedure 76. — *Precipitation of Calcium.* — Dilute the ammoniacal filtrate from the K_2CrO_4 precipitate (P. 74) with 50 cc. of water, add just 3 cc. of 3 n. $K_2C_2O_4$ solution, and, unless there is already a precipitate, let the mixture stand at least 15 minutes. (Fine white precipitate, presence of CALCIUM.)

In case there is no precipitate, treat the solution by P. 78.

In case there is a precipitate, heat the mixture nearly to boiling, and add gradually 3–10 cc. more 3 n. $K_2C_2O_4$ solution, adjusting the volume added to the size of the $(NH_4)_2CO_3$ precipitate produced in P. 71. Continue to heat the mixture for 5 minutes; then filter it immediately, and wash the precipitate. (Precipitate, P. 77; filtrate, P. 78.)

Notes. — 1. Only 3 cc. of the $K_2C_2O_4$ solution are added at first, in order to prevent, so far as is possible, the precipitation of MgC_2O_4. This volume of reagent would not precipitate magnesium unless there were present a very large quantity of it (more than 300 mg.), such as would very rarely be found (in view of the small equivalent weight of this element) in the one gram of substance taken for analysis. But if a larger volume of the reagent were used, a precipitate might result with a smaller quantity of magnesium.

2. With even this small quantity of the reagent ½ mg. of calcium gives an almost immediate precipitate when not much magnesium is present; but in the presence of a large quantity of magnesium the test is much less delicate. Thus, in order to detect 1 mg. of calcium in the presence of 300 mg. of magnesium, the mixture must be allowed to stand for ten to fifteen minutes.

3. To insure the complete precipitation of calcium, a larger volume (3–10 cc.) of the $K_2C_2O_4$ reagent is subsequently added; and, though this may cause the precipitation of some of the magnesium, this is not important since the presence or absence of calcium has already been determined.

4. The volume of $K_2C_2O_4$ solution finally added should be adjusted, not as usual to the size of the precipitate that the reagent produces, but to the sum of the quantities of calcium and magnesium that seem to be present; and since the only indication at this stage of the analysis as to the magnitude of these quantities is that afforded by the original $(NH_4)_2CO_3$ precipitate (considered in connection with the quantities of barium and strontium already found present), it is directed to adjust the added volume of the reagent (within the limits of 3–10 cc.) to the size of that precipitate.

5. The peculiar influence of magnesium in hindering the precipitation of CaC_2O_4 arises from the fact that MgC_2O_4 is far less ionized than most other salts of the same valence type, and that in consequence the $C_2O_4^=$ ion of the reagent largely combines with the Mg^{++} ion in the solution until there has been added a quantity of $K_2C_2O_4$ more than equivalent to the magnesium present.

6. The mixture is heated to boiling and the $K_2C_2O_4$ solution is added slowly, in order to cause the CaC_2O_4 to precipitate in the form of coarser particles which can be more readily filtered. The mixture is kept hot for 5 minutes to insure the complete precipitation of calcium.

7. The mixture is not heated for more than 5 minutes and is filtered immediately, in order to prevent so far as possible the precipitation of $MgC_2O_4 \cdot 2\,H_2O$. This substance, though slightly soluble in water, has an unusually great tendency to remain in supersaturated solution, especially if agitation of the solution be avoided.

8. Owing to the possibility that the precipitate formed on the first addition of $K_2C_2O_4$ may consist of magnesium or strontium oxalate, the confirmatory test for calcium given in P. 77 should not be omitted.

Procedure 77. — *Confirmatory Test for Calcium.* — Treat the $K_2C_2O_4$ precipitate (P. 76), or a small portion of it if it is large, with 5 cc. of H_2SO_4 to which 20 drops of C_2H_5OH have been added. To the solution add 10 cc. of C_2H_5OH, and let the mixture stand for several minutes. (White precipitate, presence of CALCIUM.)

Notes. — 1. $CaC_2O_4 \cdot H_2O$ is very slightly soluble in water, but reacts with dilute solutions of largely ionized acids, owing to the formation by metathesis of unionized $HC_2O_4^-$. Because of its slight solubility, only a little $CaSO_4$ dissolves in the dilute H_2SO_4, but this is completely thrown out as a flocculent precipitate by the addition to the solution of twice its volume of C_2H_5OH. One milligram of calcium produces a turbidity at once, 0.5 mg. in 1–3 minutes, and 0.2 mg. within 10 minutes. This test does not, however, furnish any indication of the quantity of calcium present except when this is very small; for whatever that quantity, not more than about 1 mg. of calcium dissolves in the mixture of 5 cc. of H_2SO_4 with 20 drops of C_2H_5OH.

2. The presence of magnesium or of strontium in the $K_2C_2O_4$ precipitate does not interfere with the test. For, even though a moderate quantity of magnesium passed into the H_2SO_4 solution, it would not precipitate on the addition of C_2H_5OH; and the quantity of strontium which dissolves in the H_2SO_4 mixture gives a barely noticeable turbidity when the two volumes of C_2H_5OH are added. A considerable turbidity

would result if the amount of strontium dissolved by the H_2SO_4 were not reduced by mixing with it the 20 drops of C_2H_5OH.

Procedure 78. — *Detection of Magnesium.* — To the filtrate from the $K_2C_2O_4$ precipitate (P. 76) add 5 cc. of 15 n. NH_4OH and 25 cc. of Na_2HPO_4 solution; cool, and shake the mixture; if no precipitate forms, let the mixture stand for at least half an hour, shaking it frequently. (White precipitate, presence of MAGNESIUM.) Filter out the precipitate, wash it once with C_2H_5OH, and treat it by P. 79.

Notes. — 1. $Mg(NH_4)PO_4$ is fairly soluble even in cold water, owing chiefly to hydrolysis into NH_4OH and $Mg^{++}HPO_4^=$. To diminish this hydrolysis the solution is made strongly ammoniacal.

2. In an aqueous solution this substance shows a great tendency to form a supersaturated solution, and it is therefore usually directed to make the test in as small a volume as possible. In the presence of C_2H_5OH, however, precipitation takes place rapidly, and even $\frac{1}{2}$ mg. of magnesium produces a distinct turbidity within half an hour under the conditions of the Procedure. A small precipitate of this kind settles out on further standing, and may then be detected by rotating the solution so as to cause the precipitate to collect in the center.

Procedure 79. — *Confirmatory Test for Magnesium.* — Treat the Na_2HPO_4 precipitate (P. 78), or a small portion of it if it is large, with 5 cc. of 2 n. H_2SO_4; add to the solution 10 cc. of C_2H_5OH, and shake it continuously for two or three minutes. Filter, if there is a precipitate; add to the filtrate 10 cc. of water, 20 cc. of NH_4OH, and 5 cc. of Na_2HPO_4 solution; and let the mixture stand at least half an hour. (White crystalline precipitate, presence of MAGNESIUM.)

Notes. — 1. This confirmatory test should be tried whenever Na_2HPO_4 produces a small precipitate that is not distinctly crystalline. For, if even a small quantity of strontium or calcium failed to be precipitated in P. 74 or 76, a flocculent precipitate of $Sr_3(PO_4)_2$ or $Ca_3(PO_4)_2$ would come down on the addition of Na_2HPO_4.

2. The addition of H_2SO_4 and C_2H_5OH precipitates strontium and calcium so completely that any precipitate (more than a very slight turbidity) produced on adding Na_2HPO_4 to the H_2SO_4 solution cannot be due to these elements.

ANALYSIS OF THE ALKALI-GROUP

GENERAL DISCUSSION

Two methods of analysis of the alkali-group are here presented. In one of these, which is called the " shorter less exact method," the two elements, potassium and sodium, are not separated, but are tested for in different portions of the solution. In the other method, called the " exact method," these elements are separated by the perchloric-acid process commonly employed in quantitative analysis. As its name implies, the first method is simpler and more rapidly executed; but it involves a less delicate, quantitative, and reliable detection of sodium than does the second method. From a pedagogic standpoint the former method will naturally be preferred, on account of its simplicity, in brief courses of instruction; and the latter method, in more thorough courses. From a practical analytical standpoint the former method is employed with advantage where the detection of small quantities of sodium is not important; but the latter method must be adopted in a complete analysis where a satisfactory detection of sodium and an approximate estimate of its quantity is desired.

SHORTER LESS EXACT METHOD

TABLE XII. — ANALYSIS OF THE ALKALI-GROUP.

Filtrate from the Ammonium Carbonate Precipitate: NH_4, K, Na salts. *Evaporate, ignite, add HCl, ignite again (P. 81).*

Vapor: NH₄ salts.	Residue: KCl, NaCl. *Add 3 cc. of water, and treat portions as follows:*	
	Add $Na_3Co(NO_2)_6$ (*P. 82*).	Add KH_2SbO_4 (*P. 83*).
	Yellow precipitate: $K_2NaCo(NO_2)_6$. *Test in flame.*	Crystalline precipitate: NaH_2SbO_4.
	Violet color: K.	

Procedure 81. — *Removal of Ammonium Salts.* — Evaporate the filtrate from the $(NH_4)_2CO_3$ precipitate (P. 71) to dryness in a small casserole, and ignite the residue, at first moderately, then to a temperature much below redness, till no more white fumes come off, keeping the dish in motion over the flame, and taking care to heat the sides as well as the bottom of the dish. Cool the dish, and pour into it 2–5 cc. of 12 n. HCl. (In case there is a considerable residue, heat the mixture to 70–80°, stirring with a glass rod to disintegrate the residue; then cool the mixture completely, and decant the solution from any crystalline residue into another casserole; adding 2 cc. more 12 n. HCl, and decanting again into the same casserole, if the residue is large enough to retain much of the solution.) Evaporate the solution to dryness, and ignite the residue as before. (White residue, presence of POTASSIUM or SODIUM.) Cool the dish, add 3 cc. of water, and pour the solution through a very small filter. Treat one-third of the solution by P. 82, and the remainder by P. 83.

Notes. — 1. Great care must be taken to volatilize the ammonium salts completely, since even 1 mg. of ammonium would give a precipitate in the subsequent test for potassium. To insure their removal the residue is ignited twice. The dish must not, however, be heated nearly to a red heat during the ignition, since at that temperature KCl and NaCl are somewhat volatile.

2. Since in the dry form even a residue that seems very small may correspond to an appreciable quantity of potassium or sodium, the subsequent tests for these elements should be made if there is any residue whatever after the final ignition.

3. A brown or black residue of organic matter, coming from impurity in the ammonium salts added in the course of analysis and from the alcohol and filter paper, may remain upon treating the ignited residue with water. There may also be a white residue of silica, coming from the action of the reagents on the glass and porcelain vessels throughout the course of the analysis.

4. The addition of the 5 cc. of 12 n. HCl serves to leave undissolved as KCl all but about 50 mg. of the potassium when a larger quantity of it is present. This is important since it makes the subsequent sodium test much more delicate. When much sodium is present a large quantity of it is also left undissolved. The ignited residue is warmed with the HCl, so as to dissolve it partially; since treatment with the acid

in the cold may extract scarcely any of a small quantity of either of the alkali-group elements from a large residue of the other.

5. Only 3 cc. of water are added to the residue after the second ignition so that the volume may be small enough to enable the subsequent test for sodium to be applied directly, without evaporating the solution.

Procedure 82. — *Detection of Potassium.* — Dilute one-third of the solution (P. 81) to 5 cc., and add an equal volume of $Na_3Co(NO_2)_6$ reagent. If no precipitate forms at once, let the mixture stand for at least 10 minutes. Filter, and wash the precipitate thoroughly with water. (Yellow precipitate, presence of POTASSIUM.)

Treat the precipitate with a 5-cc. portion of hot HCl, evaporate the solution to 1–2 drops, dip into it a clean platinum wire (which has been heated in a flame till it no longer colors it), and introduce the wire into a colorless gas flame, viewing the flame through a sufficient thickness of blue cobalt glass to cut off sodium light. (Violet flame, presence of POTASSIUM.)

Notes. — 1. The $Na_3Co(NO_2)_6$ (sodium cobaltinitrite) reagent is a solution 0.1 formal in $Na_3Co(NO_2)_6$, 3 n. in $NaNO_2$, and 1 n. in HAc.

2. The presence of 0.3 mg. of potassium in 5 cc. of solution may be detected within 5 or 10 minutes, and an even smaller amount on long standing. The yellow color of the precipitate is best seen on the filter after washing out the $Na_3Co(NO_2)_6$ thoroughly.

3. Even 0.5–1.0 mg. of ammonium produces a precipitate very similar in appearance to that given by potassium. Moderate amounts of the alkaline-earth elements do not interfere with the test.

4. The flame coloration produced by sodium is so much more delicate than that caused by potassium that the presence of a minute quantity of sodium may completely obscure the color given by a moderate amount of potassium. A sufficient thickness of blue cobalt glass is therefore used to absorb the yellow rays completely, and thus permit the violet rays due to potassium to be seen. It is necessary to use two or three pieces of the blue glass usually supplied for the purpose. Comparative experiments with known solutions ought always to be made, unless the analyst is familiar with the appearance of the flames.

5. This confirmatory flame test should not be omitted (unless the yellow precipitate is large), owing to the danger of error arising from incomplete removal of the ammonium salts in the ignitions in P. 81.

Procedure 83. — *Detection of Sodium.* — To the remaining two-thirds of the solution (P. 81) add 2 cc. of KH_2SbO_4 reagent; pour the mixture into a test-tube, and let it stand for at least half an hour, or better overnight. In case there is a flocculent precipitate, shake the mixture, and after a few seconds decant the liquid and the suspended precipitate. (White crystalline precipitate, presence of SODIUM.)

Notes. — 1. The KH_2SbO_4 (potassium dihydrogen antimonate) reagent is 0.1 molal in this salt and 0.1 normal in KOH. The alkali must be present, since the antimonate decomposes rapidly in acid solution, and slowly in neutral solution, with precipitation of H_3SbO_4 (antimonic acid). The reagent should be tested occasionally with a solution containing 1 or 2 mg. of sodium, to make sure that it is in good condition.

2. The precipitate of NaH_2SbO_4 is a heavy crystalline one, which usually adheres in part to the glass, where it can best be seen by tilting the test-tube or pouring the liquid out of it. A flocculent precipitate affords no evidence of the presence of sodium.

3. When the solution contains no other basic constituent 1 mg. of sodium is easily detected. In the presence of much potassium the test is far less delicate. Thus 3 to 10 mg. of sodium would have to be present to give a precipitate if the 2 cc. of solution contained more than 100 mg. of potassium. The treatment with HCl in P. 81, however, so decreases the quantity of potassium that can be present that 2 or 3 mg. of sodium can be detected.

4. With the KH_2SbO_4 reagent many other elements, even if present in small quantity, give precipitates. Thus a distinct turbidity is produced by even 0.1–0.2 mg. of alkaline-earth elements — quantities which might not have been removed by $(NH_4)_2CO_3$ in P. 71. These elements yield, however, light, flocculent precipitates which look very different from the heavy crystalline precipitate obtained with sodium, especially if the mixture has been allowed to stand a few hours. Even though, as is often the case, such a flocculent precipitate is produced, the presence of a crystalline precipitate can usually be detected by decanting the liquid as directed in the Procedure.

ANALYSIS OF THE ALKALI GROUP

EXACT METHOD

TABLE XIII. — ANALYSIS OF THE ALKALI-GROUP.

Filtrate from the Ammonium Carbonate Precipitate: NH_4, K, Na salts.
Evaporate, and ignite the residue. Dissolve in water, add $BaCl_2$ (to remove sulfate), then $(NH_4)_2CO_3$ (to remove barium). Evaporate and ignite again (P. 85).

Vapor: NH_4 salts.	Residue: KCl, $NaCl$. *Add $HClO_4$, evaporate, add alcohol (P. 86).*		
	Residue: $KClO_4$. *Dissolve in hot water, add $Na_3Co(NO_2)_6$ (P. 87).*	Solution: $NaClO_4$. *Saturate with HCl gas (P. 88).*	
		Precipitate: $NaCl$. *Dissolve in water, add KH_2SbO_4 (P. 89).*	Filtrate: *Reject.*
	Yellow precipitate: $K_2NaCo(NO_2)_6$.	Crystalline precipitate: NaH_2SbO_4.	

Procedure 85. — *Removal of Sulfate and of Ammonium Salts.* — Evaporate the filtrate from the $(NH_4)_2CO_3$ precipitate (P. 71) to dryness in a small casserole, and ignite the residue, at first very moderately, then to a temperature much below redness, till no more white fumes come off, keeping the dish in motion over a flame and taking care to heat the sides as well as the bottom of the dish. Cool the dish, add 5 cc. of water, transfer the solution to a flask, and add 2–10 cc. of $BaCl_2$ solution. (In case H_2SO_4 was used in P. 5 or P. 8 in the Preparation of the Solution, add enough more $BaCl_2$ solution to precipitate all the sulfate.) Heat the mixture nearly to boiling for 2 or 3 minutes, and filter out the precipitate. To the filtrate add 5–15 cc. of $(NH_4)_2CO_3$ reagent, let the mixture stand for 5 minutes, heat it nearly to boiling, and filter out the precipitate. Evaporate the filtrate to dryness in a small casserole, and ignite the residue just as before. Cool the dish, add 5 cc. of water, filter the mixture through a 5-cm. filter, evaporate the filtrate to dryness

in a small casserole, and ignite the residue as before. (White residue, presence of POTASSIUM or SODIUM.) Treat the residue by P. 86.

Notes. — 1. Sulfate must be removed before attempting to separate potassium and sodium with $HClO_4$. The process of removing it involves its precipitation as $BaSO_4$ by the addition of $BaCl_2$, the removal of the excess of barium by the subsequent addition of $(NH_4)_2CO_3$, and finally the volatilization of the ammonium salts by ignition. If phosphate is present, it is also removed by the addition of $BaCl_2$ to the neutral solution; but its removal is not essential for the $HClO_4$ separation.

2. Sulfate may be present in the $(NH_4)_2CO_3$ filtrate in considerable quantity either because sulfate (or sulfide) is a constituent of the substance submitted to analysis, or because H_2SO_4 was used in the preparation of the solution in P. 5 or P. 8. Even when it does not come from these sources, a small quantity of it is usually present at this point in the analysis, because it is produced when the $(NH_4)_2CO_3$ filtrate is evaporated to dryness and the residue is ignited, owing to the action of the nitrate present on sulfur-compounds coming from the decomposition of the $(NH_4)_2S$ reagent. The removal of sulfate is therefore made a part of the regular procedure.

3. As to the precautions to be observed in igniting the residue and as to the residue itself, see Notes 1–3, P. 81.

Procedure 86. — *Separation of Potassium and Sodium.* — To the ignited residue (P. 85) add 2–5 cc. of 6 n. $HClO_4$; and evaporate, by keeping the dish in motion over a small flame, till thick white fumes of $HClO_4$ come off copiously. Cool completely, add 10–20 cc. of 95% C_2H_5OH, and stir the mixture for 2–5 minutes if there is much residue. (White residue, presence of POTASSIUM.) Filter through a dry filter-paper, and wash the residue with a little 95% C_2H_5OH. (Precipitate, P. 87; filtrate, P. 88.)

Notes. — 1. Enough $HClO_4$ must be added to convert the potassium and sodium chlorides completely into perchlorates, and the evaporation must be continued till all the HCl is expelled; for otherwise NaCl, being insoluble in alcohol, may be left as a residue with the $KClO_4$. An unnecessary excess of $HClO_4$ is, however, to be avoided, since it makes the subsequent test for sodium somewhat less delicate. The quantity added is therefore varied (from 2 to 5 cc.) in accordance with the size of the ignited residue obtained in P. 85.

2. Another reason for continuing the evaporation till the $HClO_4$ fumes strongly is to remove most of the water; for this test for potassium and the subsequent test for sodium (in P. 88) are more delicate, the less the quantity of water present. When the directions given in the Procedure are followed, $1–1\frac{1}{2}$ mg. of potassium produces a distinct precipitate.

3. If sulfate were present and it were not removed in P. 85 by the addition of $BaCl_2$, this separation of potassium and sodium would be unsatisfactory; for Na_2SO_4 would remain in the residue undissolved by the alcohol. This arises from the fact that H_2SO_4 is less volatile than $HClO_4$ and is therefore not expelled by it in the evaporation, and from the fact that Na_2SO_4 is only slightly soluble in alcohol even in the presence of $HClO_4$.

4. The presence of phosphate or borate does not interfere with the separation; for, though phosphoric and boric acids are not volatilized in the evaporation with $HClO_4$, they are displaced from their sodium salts by the excess of $HClO_4$, since this acid is much more largely ionized than phosphoric or boric acid. The sodium therefore remains dissolved in the alcoholic solution.

Procedure 87. — *Confirmatory Test for Potassium.* — Pour repeatedly through the filter containing the $HClO_4$ precipitate (P. 86) a 5–10 cc. portion of boiling water. Cool the mixture, add to it 5 cc. of $Na_3Co(NO_2)_6$ reagent, and let it stand for 10 minutes. (Yellow precipitate, presence of POTASSIUM.)

Notes. — 1. This confirmatory test should not be omitted, owing to the possibility that the residue left undissolved by the alcohol in P. 86 consists of $NaClO_4$, $NaCl$, or Na_2SO_4. The $NaClO_4$ may result from incomplete solution of it in the C_2H_5OH, the $NaCl$ from incomplete conversion of the chlorides into perchlorates in the evaporation with $HClO_4$, and the Na_2SO_4 from the presence of sulfate which was not removed by the $BaCl_2$.

2. In regard to this test for potassium see Notes 1–3, P. 82.

Procedure 88. — *Detection of Sodium.* — Pour the alcoholic filtrate (P. 86) into a dry conical flask placed in a vessel of cold water, and pass into it a fairly rapid current of dry HCl gas (see Note 2) till the gas is no longer absorbed. (White precipitate, presence of SODIUM.) Filter through a small filter-paper. Wash the precipitate with a little 99 % C_2H_5OH, and treat it by P. 89. Reject the filtrate: *do not under any circumstances heat or evaporate it.*

Notes. — 1. This test for sodium is most delicate when the alcohol is completely saturated with HCl gas, in which case 1 mg. of sodium can be detected.

2. The dry HCl gas may be prepared by dropping 95% H_2SO_4 from a separating funnel into a flask containing solid NaCl covered with 12 n. HCl, and passing the gas through a gas-wash-bottle containing 95% H_2SO_4. Such a gas-generator may be conveniently kept ready for use in a hood in the laboratory, as the evolution of gas soon ceases when no more H_2SO_4 is added.

3. The alcoholic filtrate containing the excess of $HClO_4$ must not be heated or evaporated, since a dangerous explosion is likely to result.

Procedure 89. — *Confirmatory Test for Sodium.* — Pour a 10-cc. portion of water repeatedly through the filter containing the HCl precipitate (P. 88), evaporate the solution just to dryness, add 1 cc. of water, then KOH solution drop by drop till the mixture turns litmus paper blue, and finally 2 cc. of KH_2SbO_4 reagent. Pour the mixture into a test-tube, and let it stand for at least half an hour, preferably overnight. In case there is a flocculent precipitate, shake the mixture, and after a few seconds decant the liquid and the suspended precipitate. (White crystalline precipitate, presence of SODIUM.)

Notes. — 1. In regard to this test for sodium see the Notes on P. 83.

2. Since there is no potassium present, this test for sodium is much more delicate than the corresponding one made in the shorter method of analysis of the alkali-group.

SUPPLEMENTARY PROCEDURES FOR BASIC CONSTITUENTS

GENERAL DISCUSSION

The system of analysis for the basic constituents presented in the preceding Procedures needs to be supplemented by provision for the detection of ammonium and for the determination of the state of oxidation of certain elements.

The detection of ammonium is provided for in P. 91. Since ammonium does not occur in substances of natural origin nor in industrial products that have been made by high-temperature processes, this Procedure is omitted in analyzing such substances.

The elements forming basic constituents which commonly occur in two or more states of oxidation are mercury, iron, tin, arsenic, chromium, and manganese. A method is presented in P. 92 for determining the state of oxidation of the first three of these elements, which form the cations Hg_2^{++} and Hg^{++}, Fe^{++} and Fe^{+++}, and Sn^{++} and Sn^{++++} (also in the case of tin the corresponding anions $SnO_2^=$ and $SnO_3^=$). Arsenic is ordinarily in the form of the acidic constituents, arsenite and arsenate, forming the anions AsO_2^- and $AsO_4^{\equiv}$ (in which the arsenic has the valence 3 and 5, respectively); and these are provided for (in P. 116) in the system for the detection of acidic constituents. Chromium is commonly met with, either as a basic constituent in chromic compounds, forming the cation Cr^{+++}, or as an acid constituent in chromates, forming the anions $CrO_4^=$ and $Cr_2O_7^=$ (in which the chromium has a valence of 6). Whether or not it is present as chromate is determined in P. 111. Manganese commonly occurs as a basic constituent in manganous compounds, forming the cation Mn^{++}, as the oxide MnO_2 (in which the manganese has the valence 4), or as an acidic constituent in manganates and permanganates, forming the anions $MnO_4^=$ and MnO_4^- (in which the manganese has the valence 6 and 7, respectively). The green and purple colors of the last two of these constituents are so pronounced and undergo such marked changes in the treatment with acids (in P. 3) or with H_2S (in P. 21) that special provision is not made for their detection.

K

TABLE XIV. — SUPPLEMENTARY PROCEDURES FOR BASIC CONSTITUENTS

Boil the substance with NaOH solution (P. 91).	Boil the substance with H_2SO_4; treat portions of the solution as follows (P. 92.):				
	Add $K_3Fe(CN)_6$.	Add KSCN.	Add $HgCl_2$.	Add HCl.	
Vapor: NH_3. Absorb in water; add K_2HgI_4.	Blue precipitate: $Fe_3(Fe(CN)_6)_2$. (Shows FERROUS IRON.)	Red color: $Fe(SCN)_3$. (Shows FERRIC IRON.)	Precipitate: Hg_2Cl_2. (Shows STANNOUS TIN.)	Precipitate: Hg_2Cl_2 or AgCl. Add NH_4OH.	Filtrate. $HgCl_2$. Add $SnCl_2$
Orange precipitate: $HgO \cdot Hg_{NH_2}^{I}$. (Shows AMMONIUM.)				Black residue: Hg and $Hg_{NH_2}^{Cl}$. (Shows MERCUROUS MERCURY.)	Precipitate: Hg_2Cl_2 or Hg. (Shows MERCURIC MERCURY.)

Procedure 91. — *Detection of Ammonium.* — Place 0.2 g. of the finely powdered substance and 2 cc. of NaOH solution in a 50-cc. round-bottom flask. Insert a stopper carrying a glass rod around whose end is wound a piece of moist red litmus paper; and heat the mixture nearly to boiling. (Blue coloration of the litmus paper and odor of ammonia, presence of AMMONIUM.)

Confirmation of Ammonium. — If the litmus turns blue or the vapors smell of ammonia, pour into the flask 10 cc. of water, insert a stopper fitted with a long wide delivery-tube leading to the bottom of a test-tube placed in a vessel of cold water, and distil slowly till about half the water has passed over. To the distillate add K_2HgI_4 reagent, drop by drop, so long as the precipitate increases. (Orange precipitate, presence of AMMONIUM.)

Notes. — 1. Less than 0.2 mg. of ammonium can be detected with litmus paper and by the odor when the test is carried out as described in the first paragraph of the Procedure. The test described in the last paragraph is useful with very small quantities of ammonium as a confirmation, and with larger quantities as a means of better estimating the proportion of it present.

2. The K_2HgI_4 reagent is a solution 0.5 n. in K_2HgI_4 and 3 n. in NaOH. It is commonly called Nessler reagent.

3. The orange precipitate produced by the action of NH_3 on alkaline K_2HgI_4 is a complex compound of the composition $HgO \cdot Hg(NH_2)I$. The test is extremely delicate, a distinct precipitate resulting even with 0.2 mg. of ammonium in 5 cc. of solution, and a pronounced yellow color with a much smaller quantity. This fact must be taken into account in estimating the quantity of ammonium present.

Procedure 92. — *Determination of the State of Oxidation of Iron, Tin, and Mercury.* — In case iron, tin, or mercury has been found present, boil 20 cc. of H_2SO_4 in a small flask; drop into it 0.2 g. of the finely powdered substance. (If solution does not take place at once, boil the mixture vigorously for 2–3 minutes, covering the flask loosely with a watch-glass.) Cork the flask, cool the mixture, and treat immediately 5-cc. portions of it as follows, first pouring them through a filter if the substance has not dissolved completely.

In case iron has been found present, pour one portion into 3 cc. of $K_3Fe(CN)_6$ solution (blue precipitate, presence of FERROUS IRON); and pour another portion into 3 cc. of KSCN solution (red color, presence of FERRIC IRON).

In case tin has been found present, pour one portion into 5 cc. of 0.2 n. $HgCl_2$ solution. (White precipitate, presence of STANNOUS TIN.)

In case mercury has been found present, to one portion add 2 cc. of HCl. (White precipitate, presence of MERCUROUS MERCURY or SILVER.) Filter the mixture. Treat the precipitate on the filter with NH_4OH. (Black residue, presence of MERCUROUS MERCURY.) To the filtrate add $SnCl_2$ solution, one drop at first, then a few more drops, and finally 1–2 cc. (White precipitate, turning gray with excess of the reagent, presence of MERCURIC MERCURY.)

Notes. — 1. The H_2SO_4 is boiled before adding the substance in order to expel the air, which would oxidize stannous and ferrous salts. The mixture is afterwards boiled in order to decompose slowly dissolving substances, and in order to expel any H_2S (arising from the presence of a sulfide), which would give a precipitate with the $SnCl_2$ and $HgCl_2$.

2. If in preparing the solution for the analysis for basic constituents the substance was dissolved in water or in cold dilute HNO_3, the state

of oxidation of mercury will have been determined by its presence or absence in the HCl and H₂S precipitates. But, if the substance was treated with hot or concentrated HNO_3, any mercurous compound present will have been partly or completely oxidized to the mercuric state.

DETECTION OF THE ACIDIC CONSTITUENTS

GENERAL DISCUSSION

THE acidic constituents whose detection is here provided for are

Arsenate	Chromate	Nitrate
Arsenite	Cyanide	Nitrite
Borate	Ferrocyanide	Oxalate
Bromide	Ferricyanide	Sulfate
Carbonate	Fluoride	Sulfide
Chlorate	Hypochlorite	Sulfite
Chloride	Iodide	Thiocyanate

Provision has already been made for detecting phosphate and silicate in the course of the analysis for basic constituents.

Different processes are described in this book for the detection of the acidic constituents, according as the substance is, on the one hand, an industrial product that has been made by a high-temperature process or a substance that is of natural origin; or, on the other hand, an industrial product that has been separated from solutions or prepared by other low-temperature process. The first of these classes of substances will be called *natural substances and igneous products;* the second, *non-igneous products.* The first class includes all minerals, ores, and rocks (except water-soluble salt-deposits); slags, mattes, and other metallurgical products; and glasses, porcelains, refractories, abrasives, and other ceramic products. The second class includes all other industrial products, such as chemicals, pigments, fertilizers, and commercial preparations.

The main reason for this differentiation is that water-insoluble minerals and high-temperature products contain only a comparatively small number of acidic constituents; namely, carbonate, sulfide, sulfate, chloride, fluoride, borate, phosphate, and silicate, and rarely cyanide; so that a much simpler procedure can be followed than when any acidic constituent whatever may be present. A second reason is that these natural and igneous substances are, as a rule, decomposed with more difficulty than most industrial products, making necessary the use of strong acids in place of the treatment with sodium carbonate solution, which is best employed in preparing a solution for testing for acidic constituents in the more reactive substances.

In the following system of analysis non-igneous products are first considered, since a survey of the methods of detection of all the acidic constituents is thereby obtained. (See Tables XV–XX.) The much shorter process required for the detection of the small number of constituents that may occur in natural substances or igneous products is then presented. (See Tables XXI and XXII.)

It is to be noted that the system of procedure for detecting the acidic constituents can often be much shortened by omitting the tests for certain constituents which are excluded by the solubility of the substance considered in connection with the basic constituents present. Thus, in a neutral water-soluble substance containing barium or silver it is unnecessary to test for any of the acidic constituents which form insoluble compounds with these elements. A General Statement as to the Solubilities of substances in water and dilute acids will be found in the Appendix.

Metals and alloys do not contain any of the ordinary acidic constituents, but they may contain the elements carbon, phosphorus, and silicon in considerable proportion. These are commonly detected in the course of the analysis for basic constituents.

Procedure 100. — *General Directions.* — In case the substance is a non-igneous product, proceed as follows :

Treat a sample of the substance by P. 101, to prepare a solution for the detection (by P. 102–116) of most of the acidic constituents.

Treat a sample of the substance by P. 117, heating it with dilute HCl and Zn, and testing the distillate for carbonate and sulfide.

In case the substance is a natural substance or igneous product, proceed as follows :

Treat a sample of the substance by P. 121, distilling it with dilute HCl and Zn; testing the mixture remaining in the flask for sulfate, and the distillate for carbonate, sulfide, and cyanide.

Treat a sample of the substance by P. 122, distilling it with H_2SO_4, first alone and then with methyl alcohol, to detect chloride, fluoride, and borate.

If the substance after treatment with HNO_3 and HCl in P. 2 and 3 left a residue that has been fused with Na_2CO_3 (by P. 7), treat the aqueous extract of the fused mass as described in P. 123, to detect sulfate, fluoride, borate, and silicate.

In case the substance is a solution, treat it as described in the last two paragraphs of P. 9.

Notes. — 1. The reasons for adopting distinct systems of procedures for " non-igneous products " and for " natural substances and igneous products," and the significance of these terms as here used, have been explained in the General Discussion on the preceding pages.

2. The much smaller number of constituents that need to be tested for in the latter class of substances has been there referred to. They are the seven whose detection is provided for in the second section of this Procedure; and in addition, silicate, phosphate, and arsenate, which are ordinarily detected in the analysis for basic constituents.

ANALYSIS OF NON-IGNEOUS PRODUCTS

PREPARATION OF THE SOLUTION AND DIRECTIONS FOR ITS TREATMENT

Procedure 101. — *Preparation of a Solution by Boiling the Substance with Sodium Carbonate Solution.* — Place in a casserole $2\frac{1}{2}$ g. of the finely powdered substance and 25 cc. of 3 n. Na_2CO_3 solution; cover the casserole, and boil the mixture very gently for 5–10 minutes, replacing the water if much evaporates. (See Notes 3 and 4.) Filter. Wash the residue, and reserve it for treatment by P. 117 in certain cases. Dilute the solution to just 30 cc., and treat portions of it as follows:

Treat 1-cc. portions of the solution by P. 102, 104, and 105, and a 2-cc. portion by P. 103, to detect certain groups of acidic constituents.

In case in P. 102 the chloride-group is found present, treat a 6-cc. portion by P. 106–110, to detect the separate constituents of that group.

In case in P. 103 the sulfate-group is found present, treat a 6-cc. portion by P. 111–112, to detect the separate constituents of that group.

In case in P. 104 oxidizing constituents are found present, treat a 2-cc. portion by P. 113, to detect nitrate or nitrite; and, if found present, treat a 1-cc. portion by P. 114, to detect nitrite.

In every case treat a 3-cc. portion by P. 115, to detect borate.

In case in P. 44 arsenic was found present, treat a 3-cc. portion by P. 116, to detect arsenate and arsenite.

Notes. — 1. The treatment with Na_2CO_3 serves two purposes. In the case of water-soluble salts, it precipitates and removes from the solution all the basic constituents, except potassium and sodium and certain amphoteric elements; and in the case of most water-insoluble compounds, it causes metathesis, the acidic constituent combining with the sodium and passing into the solution, and the basic constituent combining with the carbonate and being precipitated. Thus $PbSO_4$ is metathesized with formation of soluble Na_2SO_4 and solid $PbCO_3$.

2. The removal of the basic constituents is desirable, since many of them would interfere with the tests for acidic constituents by producing precipitates with the reagents added or imparting colors to the solution. Thus, if an aqueous or HNO_3 solution of the substance were tested directly, silver and mercurous mercury would precipitate whenever any chloride is added; bismuth, aluminum, chromium, and ferric iron might separate when to a HNO_3 solution NaAc is added; and copper, nickel, cobalt, iron, and chromium would by their own colors interfere with the color test for borate.

3. In case the only basic constituents present are potassium, sodium, and ammonium, an aqueous solution of the substance may be used for the tests for the acidic constituents, in place of the solution prepared by boiling with Na_2CO_3 solution.

4. In case the substance is already in aqueous solution, to that volume of the solution which contains 2.5 g. of solid matter (as found in P. 9) 25 cc. of 3 n. Na_2CO_3 solution are added, the mixture is evaporated, made up to just 30 cc., and filtered, and portions of the filtrate are treated by P. 102–116.

5. Many sulfides are not decomposed by the Na_2CO_3 solution. Even the sulfides of elements of the iron group are very little acted upon. Further provision is therefore made (in P. 117) for the detection of sulfide by treating the original substance or the residue undissolved by Na_2CO_3 solution with HCl and Zn.

6. Of other substances that may not be attacked the following may be mentioned. Many of the phosphates are but slightly acted upon by Na_2CO_3 solution; and it is therefore advantageous that phosphate has already been tested for in an acid solution of the substance in the course of the analysis for basic constituents. $BaSO_4$ also may be only partially decomposed; but it is acted upon sufficiently to yield a good test for sulfate. Finally, the halides of silver are not affected much by the Na_2CO_3 solution.

7. The principles involved in the metathesizing action of Na_2CO_3 solution are as follows. The extent to which the metathesis of a slightly soluble salt (like $PbSO_4$) takes place is determined by the ratio of the saturation-values of the ion-concentration product for the salt and for the corresponding carbonate ($PbCO_3$ in case of $PbSO_4$). For as explained in Note 6, P. 11, in any solution saturated with respect to these substances the following mass-action expressions, in which S_{PbSO_4} and S_{PbCO_3} represent the solubilities of $PbSO_4$ and $PbCO_3$ in pure water at any given temperature, must both be satisfied:

$$(Pb^{++}) \times (SO_4^{=}) = (S_{PbSO_4})^2; \text{ and } (Pb^{++}) \times (CO_3^{=}) = (S_{PbCO_3})^2.$$

Dividing the first of these equations by the second, we get the following:

$$(SO_4^=)/(CO_3^=) = (S_{PbSO_4})^2/(S_{PbCO_3})^2.$$

This expression shows that $PbSO_4$ will be metathesized by Na_2CO_3 solution until the concentration of sulfate-ion bears the same ratio to the concentration of carbonate-ion in the solution as the square of the solubility of $PbSO_4$ bears to the square of the solubility of $PbCO_3$ in pure water. Since, as will be seen by referring to the Table of Solubilities in the Appendix, this ratio for $PbSO_4$ and $PbCO_3$ has at 20° the very large value 490,000, it is evident that $PbSO_4$ will be completely transformed into $PbCO_3$ at 20° by even a small excess of Na_2CO_3 before this equilibrium ratio of $(SO_4^=)$ to $(CO_3^=)$ is established in the solution. But in the case of the salt $BaSO_4$, the ratio of the squares of the solubilities has, as will be seen from the table, the small value 0.01, which shows that the conversion of $BaSO_4$ into $BaCO_3$ will cease when the concentration of sulfate-ion becomes only 1% of that of carbonate-ion. Still, by making the latter concentration large, as we do by using a large excess of Na_2CO_3 solution, a considerable quantity even of $BaSO_4$ will be metathesized before the conditions of equilibrium are established. — It is to be noted that the form of the mass-action expression depends on the valences of the two ions of the salt that is subjected to the action of the Na_2CO_3 solution. Thus the expression is different for salts of the four valence types exemplified by $PbSO_4$, PbI_2, Ag_2SO_4, and AgI. The corresponding expressions can be readily derived by the method illustrated above in the case of $PbSO_4$. It may also be noted that basic carbonates are often formed; thus lead salts really yield $PbCO_3$. $xPb(OH)_2$ with Na_2CO_3; but this does not greatly modify the theory of the metathesis described above.

8. Besides the elements which form only acidic constituents, those which form both basic and acidic constituents may be present in the Na_2CO_3 solution. Thus, manganese, chromium, and arsenic may be present as sodium permanganate, chromate, arsenate, and arsenite. Certain elements which form amphoteric hydroxides, like aluminum, chromium, antimony, tin, and copper, may also pass in small quantity into the Na_2CO_3 solution.

9. Certain acidic constituents may be converted into other constituents by boiling Na_2CO_3 solution. Hypochlorite, when present alone, decomposes into chloride and chlorate. If it were present with a reducing acidic constituent (namely, with sulfide, sulfite, or arsenite), or with reducing basic constituents (namely, with lead, antimony, stannous tin, ferrous iron, nickel, cobalt, chromium, and manganese), it would be converted into chloride. Ferricyanide is converted into

ferrocyanide, and permanganate into MnO_2, by most of these reducing substances. Chromate is reduced by sulfide and arsenite, and by stannous tin and ferrous iron. Chlorate, nitrate, and nitrite are not reduced in alkaline solution by other acidic constituents. Sulfide and sulfite do not act upon one another in boiling Na_2CO_3 solution, though they do so instantly on acidification.

10. It is unnecessary, however, to provide for detecting hypochlorite, ferricyanide, permanganate, or chromate when any of the mentioned reducing substances that react with them in boiling Na_2CO_3 solution is present; for, on account of their general incompatibility, such combinations are not met with in industrial products. Ferricyanide and chromate will therefore be found as such in the Na_2CO_3 solution in all practical cases; and hypochlorite need be tested for (by P. 108, on a fresh sample of the substance) only when both chloride and chlorate are found present, and when the reducing substances incompatible with it are absent.

11. The constituents, sulfide, sulfite, nitrite, and iodide, which in HCl or H_2SO_4 solution are strong reducing agents, are destroyed in the boiling Na_2CO_3 solutions only by the most powerful oxidizing agents, — hypochlorite, ferricyanide, and permanganate (and by chromate in the case of sulfide). Sulfite, however, is always partially converted into sulfate by the oxygen of the air.

BEHAVIOR OF THE ACIDIC CONSTITUENTS TOWARD GROUP
REAGENTS

TABLE XV. — DETECTION OF GROUPS OF ACIDIC CONSTITUENTS.

Sodium Carbonate Solution Containing All Acidic Constituents (P. 101).
Treat portions as follows:

Add $AgNO_3$, $NaNO_2$, and HNO_3 (P. 102).	Add HAc, $BaCl_2$, and $CaCl_2$ (P. 103).	Add $MnCl_2$ and HCl (P. 104).	Add HCl, $FeCl_3$, and $K_3Fe(CN)_6$ (P. 105).
Precipitate: CHLORIDE-GROUP (S, CN, $Fe(CN)_6^{IV}$, $Fe(CN)_6^{III}$, SCN, Cl, Br, I, ClO_3, ClO), as Ag salts.	Precipitate: SULFATE-GROUP (SO_4, SO_3, CrO_4, F, C_2O_4), as Ba and Ca salts.	Dark Color: $MnCl_3$. Shows OXIDIZING CONSTITUENTS: $Fe(CN)_6^{III}$, ClO_3, ClO, CrO_4, NO_3, NO_2.	Blue precipitate: $Fe_4(Fe(CN)_6)_3$. Shows REDUCING CONSTITUENTS: S, $Fe(CN)_6^{IV}$, I, SO_3, NO_2.

Procedure 102. — *Detection of the Chloride-Group.* — To 1 cc.
of the Na_2CO_3 solution (P. 101) add 5 cc. of water, 3 drops of
(chloride-free) 3 n. $NaNO_2$ solution, 1 cc. of $AgNO_3$ solution,
and 2 cc. of HNO_3.   (Precipitate, presence of CHLORIDE-GROUP.)

Notes. — 1. In case no precipitate results, it shows the absence of
all the constituents of the chloride-group; for the silver salts of all
these (except those of chlorate and hypochlorite, which on acidification
are reduced to chloride by the $NaNO_2$ added) are only very slightly
soluble even in dilute HNO_3. In this case the subsequent procedures
(namely, P. 106–110) for detecting these constituents may be omitted.

2. The color of the precipitate may indicate the presence of certain
constituents; thus Ag_2S is black; AgI, yellow; $AgBr$, light yellow;
$Ag_3Fe(CN)_6$, orange; $AgCl$, $Ag_2(CN)_2$, $AgSCN$, and $Ag_4Fe(CN)_6$,
white.

3. It will be seen from the Table of Ionization-Values in the Appendix that all the acids of the chloride-group, except H_2S, HCN, and
$HClO$, are largely ionized. Consequently, their silver salts would be
expected to be only slightly more soluble in dilute HNO_3 than in water;
and this is the case. Ag_2S and $Ag_2(CN)_2$, however, being salts of slightly
ionized acids, might be expected to dissolve easily in dilute HNO_3 in
virtue of the tendency of its H^+ ion to form unionized H_2S or HCN

with the $S^=$ or CN^- ion of the salt. That they do not so dissolve arises from exceptional conditions. Ag_2S is not much soluble in dilute HNO_3 because its solubility in pure water is so extremely small that there is only a very minute concentration of $S^=$ ion in the saturated solution, and this can yield, in accordance with the mass-action law, only a relatively small concentration of HS^- and unionized H_2S with the H^+ ion of the HNO_3. Silver cyanide has for another reason a very slight concentration of its anion in its saturated solution; namely because this salt exists mainly as Ag^+ and $Ag(CN)_2^-$, and scarcely at all as Ag^+ and CN^- ions.

4. The other silver salts either are very soluble or moderately soluble in water (as are the nitrate, chlorate, fluoride, and sulfate), or in neutral solution they form precipitates which dissolve readily in dilute HNO_3, owing to displacement by it of the less ionized acid (as do the carbonate, sulfite, nitrite, borate, chromate, oxalate, phosphate, arsenate, and arsenite).

Procedure 103.—*Detection of the Sulfate-Group.*—Dilute 2 cc. of the Na_2CO_3 solution (P. 101) with 2 cc. of water, and add HAc, first 5 drops at a time till the mixture reddens litmus paper, and then as much more as has already been added. Filter out any precipitate. Add 1 cc. of $BaCl_2$ solution and 3 cc. of (sulfate-free) $CaCl_2$ solution, heat the mixture nearly to boiling, and let it stand for at least 10 minutes. (Precipitate, presence of SULFATE-GROUP.)

Notes.— 1. In case no precipitate results, it shows the absence of the sulfate-group; and the subsequent Procedures (P. 111–112) for detecting the separate constituents may be omitted. But in order that this conclusion and this omission may be justifiable, it is necessary to follow the directions carefully; namely, to neutralize fairly exactly with HAc and add only the specified excess, and to add the rather large quantity of $CaCl_2$ solution and allow the mixture to stand; for otherwise fluoride, oxalate, and chromate, when present in small quantity, may fail to give a precipitate. Moreover, a slight turbidity or opalescence must not be disregarded.

2. This test depends on the following facts in regard to solubility. $BaSO_4$ is very slightly soluble in water and in dilute solutions of even largely ionized acids. $BaSO_3$ and $BaCrO_4$ are also very slightly soluble in water; but, since the HSO_3^- and $HCrO_4^-$ ions are rather slightly ionized, these salts are fairly soluble in solutions of largely ionized acids such as HCl or HNO_3, but are not much dissolved by solutions of a

slightly ionized acid, such as HAc, in the presence of one of its neutral salts, such as NaAc. BaF$_2$ and BaC$_2$O$_4$ are considerably soluble in water, but CaF$_2$ and CaC$_2$O$_4$ are very slightly soluble in it. The solubilities of these two calcium salts are, however, increased by the presence of H$^+$ ion, though not very greatly by the small concentration of it existing in a HAc solution containing NaAc.

3. From a neutral solution BaCl$_2$ would give precipitates also with phosphate, arsenate, arsenite, borate, and carbonate; but none of these separates from a solution containing proper quantities of HAc and NaAc. The possibility of such precipitation fixes, however, a limit beyond which the hydrogen-ion concentration may not be diminished.

Procedure 104. — *Detection of Oxidizing Acidic Constituents.* — To 1 cc. of the Na$_2$CO$_3$ solution (P. 101) add gradually 4 cc. of a saturated solution of MnCl$_2$ in 12 n. HCl, and heat the mixture nearly to boiling. (Dark brown or black color, presence of NITRATE, NITRITE, CHLORATE, HYPOCHLORITE, CHROMATE, PERMANGANATE, or FERRICYANIDE; no brown or black color, absence of all these constituents, unless in P. 105 reducing constituents are found present.)

Notes. — 1. This simple test depends upon the fact that all these oxidizing acidic constituents convert MnCl$_2$ into the dark-colored MnCl$_3$.

2. The test determines at once the absence of all or the presence of one or more of the constituents which can act as oxidizing agents. Hence, when it gives a negative result, it enables all the procedures for detecting these constituents to be omitted, unless in P. 105 reducing constituents are found to be present. In that case a negative result is inconclusive, and the corresponding procedures must not be omitted; for the reducing effect may counteract the effect of the oxidizing constituent on the MnCl$_2$. Thus, if nitrate or chlorate were present in the alkaline solution together with an excess of sulfide or sulfite, the latter would on acidification reduce the nitrate or chlorate and prevent it from oxidizing the MnCl$_2$.

Procedure 105. — *Detection of Reducing Acidic Constituents.* — Add 1 cc. of the Na$_2$CO$_3$ solution (P. 101) to a mixture of 3 cc. of water, 1 cc. of HCl, 2 drops of Fe(NO$_3$)$_3$ solution, and 2 drops of K$_3$Fe(CN)$_6$ solution; and let the mixture stand 2 or

3 minutes. (Blue precipitate or green coloration, presence of SULFIDE, FERROCYANIDE, IODIDE, SULFITE, or NITRITE; no blue precipitate or green coloration, absence of all these constituents.)

Notes. — 1. This test depends on the facts: (1) that ferricyanide forms no precipitate with ferric salts; (2) that ferricyanide is reduced to ferrocyanide by substances with even moderate reducing power (that is, by those with fairly small reduction-potentials); and (3) that ferric salts give a dark-blue precipitate of ferric ferrocyanide with soluble ferrocyanides. The tendency of the ferricyanide to be reduced is greatly increased (since its reduction-potential is greatly decreased) by the fact that in the presence of ferric salts the ferrocyanide-ion is kept at an extremely small concentration, owing to the very slight solubility of ferric ferrocyanide. In the case of sulfite the ferric salt is more rapidly reduced than the ferricyanide; but this also results in the formation of a blue precipitate, consisting in this case mainly of ferrous ferricyanide.

2. Under the conditions of this Procedure the test is delicate enough to detect in the 1 cc. of Na_2CO_3 solution treated the presence of 0.1 mg. of any of the reducing constituents or about 0.1% of these constituents in the substance. Hence, if the test gives negative results, all these constituents may be assumed absent and the subsequent Procedures modified accordingly. Even when in P. 104 oxidizing constituents were found present, a negative result is fairly conclusive; for only those oxidizing agents, which, like permanganate, chromate, and hypochlorite, are so powerful as to be practicably incompatible with reducing constituents even in solid substances, destroy the reducing constituents rapidly enough to prevent them from acting upon the $K_3Fe(CN)_6$.

3. In the case of an effect so slight that it is doubtful whether there is a green coloration it is well to compare the color with that produced by adding to 1 cc. of pure 3 n. Na_2CO_3 solution the volumes of water and of reagents named in the Procedure. If a red color results (owing to the presence of thiocyanate), the presence or absence of a blue precipitate in the mixture may be determined by filtering it.

4. The $K_3Fe(CN)_6$ reagent should be frequently prepared freshly from the crystals, since exposure to light slowly reduces it to $K_4Fe(CN)_6$; and the presence of this substance, even in small proportion, must obviously diminish the reliability and delicacy of the test.

ANALYSIS OF THE CHLORIDE-GROUP

TABLE XVI. — SEPARATION OF THE CHLORIDE-GROUP INTO SUBGROUPS.

Sodium Carbonate Solution Containing All Acidic Constituents.
To a portion add Pb(NO₃)₂ (P. 106).

Black Precipitate: PbS. (Shows SULFIDE.)	Filtrate. *Add HAc and Ni(NO₃)₂ (P. 106).*		
	Precipitate: Ni₂Fe(CN)₆, Ni₃(Fe(CN)₆)₂, Ni(CN)₂. (Shows simple or complex CYANIDE.) See Table XVII.	Filtrate: NaSCN, NaI, NaBr, NaCl, NaClO₃. *Add AgNO₃ and HNO₃ (P. 107).*	
		Precipitate: AgSCN, AgI, AgBr, AgCl. (Shows HALIDE or THIOCYANATE.) See Table XVIII.	Filtrate: AgClO₃. *Add NaNO₂ (P. 108).*
			Precipitate: AgCl. (Shows CHLORATE or HYPOCHLORITE.)

Procedure 106. — *Precipitation of Sulfide and of the Cyanides.* — In case in P. 102 AgNO₃ produced a precipitate, treat 6 cc. of the Na₂CO₃ solution (P. 101) as follows:

Add 5 cc. of water and 1 drop of Pb(NO₃)₂ solution, and shake the mixture. (White precipitate, absence of SULFIDE; gray or black precipitate, presence of SULFIDE.) If a gray or black precipitate forms, add Pb(NO₃)₂ solution, 1 cc. at a time, shaking after each addition, till the precipitate begins to get lighter colored, not adding more than 12 cc. in all. Filter out the precipitate.

To the filtrate add HAc, 10 drops at a time, till the mixture reddens litmus paper, and then one-third as much more HAc as has already been added; and filter out any precipitate that may separate. To the solution add 3–10 cc. of Ni(NO₃)₂ solution, and let the mixture stand at least 10 minutes with frequent shaking. (Precipitate, presence of CYANIDE or of FERRO or FER-

RICYANIDE.) Filter the mixture, preferably with the aid of gentle suction if the precipitate is large (see Note 6). Wash the precipitate thoroughly. (Filtrate, P. 107; precipitate, P. 109.)

Notes. — 1. The addition of $Pb(NO_3)_2$ serves not only to detect sulfide, but to remove it (as far as possible), so that it may not precipitate with the $Ni(NO_3)_2$ and $AgNO_3$ in the subsequent operations. It is added before the solution is acidified; for otherwise, much H_2S would be lost during the effervescence caused by the escape of the CO_2, and sulfite or nitrite, if present, would immediately destroy the sulfide with liberation of sulfur.

2. The precipitation of PbS from the Na_2CO_3 solution depends on the fact that, though $PbCO_3$ is a very slightly soluble salt, PbS is very much less soluble (see the Table of Solubilities in the Appendix). Consequently, conversion of the former into the latter salt takes place, in accordance with the principles presented in Note 7, P. 101, until the concentration-ratio $(S^=)/(CO_3^=)$ attains a definite value, which in this case is of very small magnitude. A small quantity of sulfide does, however, remain in solution; and this commonly gives a small dark precipitate when $AgNO_3$ is subsequently added to precipitate the halides.

3. As most of the common sulfides are not attacked by Na_2CO_3 solution, non-formation of a precipitate does not show the absence of sulfide in the substance. The original substance or the residue insoluble in Na_2CO_3 solution must therefore also be tested for it by P. 117, as was directed in P. 100.

4. Certain substances soluble in Na_2CO_3 solution, but not soluble in the HAc solution, may precipitate on neutralizing the alkaline solution with HAc; for example, antimony or tin hydroxide; sulfur, from a persulfide or thiosulfate; H_2SiO_3 arising from silica or a silicate; $Ni(CN)_2$, $Ag_2(CN)_2$, or other cyanide, previously held in solution by KCN or NaCN.

5. Since $Ni(CN)_2$ is slightly soluble in HAc solutions and since it tends to remain in the colloidal state, at least 3 cc. of $Ni(NO_3)_2$ should be added so as to diminish its solubility, even when no precipitate results on the first addition, and the mixture should be allowed to stand at least 10 minutes, and preferably for a longer time.

6. The precipitates produced with cyanide and ferro and ferricyanide by $Ni(NO_3)_2$ solution are slimy, and are sometimes very difficult to filter. If this proves to be the case, paper-pulp, prepared as described in Note 4, P. 74, may be added to the filtrate and after vigorous shaking the mixture again filtered.

Procedure 107. — *Precipitation of the Halides.* — To the filtrate from the $Ni(NO_3)_2$ precipitate (P. 106) add 5 cc. of HNO_3 and 1–8 cc. of $AgNO_3$ solution. (If there is a black precipitate, add 3 cc. more HNO_3, and boil the mixture gently for a minute or two.) (White precipitate, presence of CHLORIDE or THIO-CYANATE; yellow precipitate, presence of BROMIDE or IODIDE.) Filter, and wash the precipitate. (Filtrate, P. 108; precipitate, P. 110.)

> *Notes.* — 1. As to the solubilities of silver salts on which this separation of the halides and thiocyanate from other constituents depends, see the Notes on P. 102.
>
> 2. Since chloride is a common impurity, care must be taken to use throughout this analysis of the chloride-group reagents that are as free as possible from chloride. And, when $AgNO_3$ produces a small precipitate, a blank test should be made by mixing with 2 cc. of $AgNO_3$ solution, in succession, 5-cc. portions of HNO_3, of 3 n. Na_2CO_3 solution, of HAc, and of $Ni(NO_3)_2$ solution.
>
> 3. A black precipitate may be produced by $AgNO_3$ when sulfide is present in the substance, owing to the fact that it was not completely precipitated by $Pb(NO_3)_2$ in P. 106. Such a precipitate dissolves, however, when more HNO_3 is added and the mixture is heated.

Procedure 108. — *Detection of Chlorate and Hypochlorite.* — To the filtrate, in case oxidizing acidic constituents were found present in P. 104, add a few drops more $AgNO_3$ solution and 5 to 20 drops of (chloride-free) 3 n. $NaNO_2$ solution. (White precipitate, presence of CHLORATE or HYPOCHLORITE.)

In case $AgNO_3$ produced a precipitate both before and after the addition of $NaNO_2$ solution, treat 0.5 g. of the powdered original substance with 10 cc. of cold water, filter the mixture, and treat the filtrate as follows: To one-half add HAc, a few drops at a time, until the solution is acid; then add about 3 cc. of $PbAc_2$ solution, heat the mixture to boiling, and let it stand 5 minutes. (Brown precipitate, presence of HYPOCHLORITE.) In case hypochlorite is found present, to the other half of the filtrate add 20 cc. of water, 5 cc. of HNO_3, 5 cc. of $NaAsO_2$ solution, and 5 cc. of $AgNO_3$ solution; and filter, rejecting the precipitate. To the filtrate add a few drops more $AgNO_3$ solution and 1 cc. of (chloride-free) 3 n. $NaNO_2$ solution. (White precipitate, presence of CHLORATE.)

Notes. — 1. The reduction of chlorate to chloride by HNO_2 is so rapid, even in the cold, that 0.5 mg. of ClO_3 produces a precipitate in a few seconds. The $NaNO_2$ may produce a precipitate of $AgNO_2$; but this dissolves on shaking the mixture. Before the addition of the $NaNO_2$ a few drops of $AgNO_3$ are added, to make sure that the halides have been completely precipitated.

2. The formation of a precipitate with $NaNO_2$ may arise from the presence in the substance either of chlorate or of hypochlorite. Since hypochlorite is changed to chloride and chlorate by boiling with Na_2CO_3 solution, it is directed to test a fresh sample of the substance for hypochlorite and chlorate in case $AgNO_3$ produced a precipitate both before and after the addition of $NaNO_2$. This need be done, however, only in case also reducing constituents incompatible with hypochlorite are not present, as described in Notes 9–11 of P. 101.

3. This test for hypochlorite depends on the oxidation of the lead salt to PbO_2 by the unionized $HClO$, which is set free by the more largely ionized HAc. The solution is acidified with HAc, rather than with HNO_3, since the oxidation does not take place in the presence of much hydrogen-ion. The test is not made in the unneutralized solution, even though it would then be somewhat more delicate, because in the presence of hydroxide-ion peroxide and ferricyanide also oxidize lead salts to PbO_2.

4. In the chlorate test the $NaAsO_2$ added reduces the hypochlorite immediately to chloride, but does not affect the chlorate. After removing with $AgNO_3$ the chloride so produced, the chlorate is reduced to chloride by $NaNO_2$.

TABLE XVII. — DETECTION OF THE SEPARATE CYANIDES.

Nickel Precipitate: $Ni_2Fe(CN)_6$, $Ni_3(Fe(CN)_6)_2$, $Ni(CN)_2$.
   Add NH_4OH (P. *109*).

Solution: $(NH_3)_4Ni(OH)_2$, $(NH_4)_4Fe(CN)_6$, $(NH_4)_3Fe(CN)_6$, NH_4CN.
   Add $AgNO_3$ and Na_2SO_3.

Precipitate: $Ag_4Fe(CN)_6$. Add HCl and $Fe(NO_3)_3$.	Filtrate: $NH_4Ag(CN)_2$, $Ni(NO_3)_2$, $AgNO_3$, and NH_4NO_3. Add HNO_3.		
Blue residue: $Fe_4(Fe(CN)_6)_3$ and AgCl. (Shows FERRO or FERRICYANIDE.)	Precipitate: $Ag_2(CN)_2$. Add $(NH_4)_2S$.		Filtrate: Ni, Ag, and NH_4 nitrates. *Reject.*
	Residue: Ag_2S. *Reject.*	Solution: NH_4CNS. Add $Fe(NO_3)_3$.	
		Red color: $Fe(CNS)_3$. (Shows CYANIDE.)	

Procedure 109. — *Detection of the Different Cyanides.* — Pour over the $Ni(NO_3)_2$ precipitate (P. 106) in a casserole a 10-cc. portion of 3 n. NH_4OH, stir the mixture, filter it if necessary, and add to it 2–5 cc. of $AgNO_3$ solution, then Na_2SO_3 solution, a few drops at a time till any brown color disappears, shaking after each addition. (White precipitate, presence of FERRO or FERRICYANIDE.) Filter the mixture.

Treat the precipitate on the filter with a mixture of 1 cc. of HCl and 1 cc. of $Fe(NO_3)_3$ solution. (Blue residue, presence of FERRO or FERRICYANIDE.)

To the filtrate from the $AgNO_3$ precipitate add HNO_3 gradually till the odor of NH_3 disappears, then 5 cc. more. (White precipitate, presence of CYANIDE.) Filter, rejecting the filtrate. Pour repeatedly through the filter a 5-cc. portion of $(NH_4)_2S$ reagent, evaporate the solution just to dryness, and add to the residue 2 cc. of HCl and 2 cc. of $Fe(NO_3)_3$ solution. (Red color, presence of CYANIDE.)

In case it is found that either ferro or ferricyanide is present, to 1 cc. of the Na_2CO_3 solution (P. 101) add 5 cc. of water, 1 cc. of HNO_3, and 1 cc. of $Fe(NO_3)_3$ solution. (Dark blue precipitate, presence of FERROCYANIDE.) Filter the mixture, repeatedly if necessary; and add to the filtrate 1 cc. of $FeCl_2$ solution. (Dark blue precipitate, presence of FERRICYANIDE.)

Notes. — 1. This separation of ferro and ferricyanide from cyanide depends upon the fact that the cyanide of silver is moderately soluble in NH_4OH, while the ferrocyanide is only very slightly soluble in it. Silver ferricyanide is also moderately soluble in NH_4OH, but it is reduced to the ferrocyanide by the Na_2SO_3 added.

2. It is not practicable to separate ferro and ferricyanide by filtering out the silver ferrocyanide before adding Na_2SO_3 and then adding this reagent to the filtrate, for the reason that the ferricyanide is reduced, at least partially, by the ammoniacal nickel solution alone. It is desirable to confirm the presence of ferro or ferricyanide by treating the $AgNO_3$ precipitate with $Fe(NO_3)_3$, since that precipitate may consist of $Ag_2(CN)_2$, which is only moderately soluble in dilute NH_4OH.

3. Owing to the possible presence of a little chloride arising from contamination or from incomplete washing of the $Ni(NO_3)_2$ precipitate, it is essential to confirm the presence of cyanide in any precipitate produced by the HNO_3. The confirmatory test depends upon the fact that $Ag_2(CN)_2$ is metathesized by $(NH_4)_2S$, yielding Ag_2S as a residue and NH_4CN in solution, and that the latter is converted during the evaporation by the liberated sulfur into NH_4CNS, which then gives a red color with the ferric salt.

4. The process for distinguishing ferro and ferricyanide described in the last paragraph of the Procedure is based on the following facts. With ferrocyanide ferric salts give a dark blue precipitate of ferric ferrocyanide (Prussian blue), while with ferricyanide they give no precipitate. With ferrocyanide ferrous salts give a precipitate (of ferrous ferrocyanide), which is white if no ferric salt is present, but which, owing to slight oxidation, is usually light-blue; with ferricyanide ferrous salts give a dark-blue precipitate, consisting mainly of ferrous ferricyanide.

TABLE XVIII. — DETECTION OF THIOCYANATE, IODIDE, BROMIDE, AND CHLORIDE.

Silver Precipitate: AgSCN, AgI, AgBr, AgCl.
Treat with NH_4OH and $(NH_4)_2S$ (P. 110).

Residue: Ag_2S.	Solution: NH_4SCN, NH_4I, NH_4Br, NH_4Cl. *Add HNO_3, $Fe(NO_3)_3$, and CCl_4.*			
	CCl_4 layer: I_2. (Purple color shows IODIDE.)	Water layer: I_2, HBr, HCl, $Fe(SCN)_3$. (Red color shows THIOCYANATE.) *Boil; then cool and add $KMnO_4$ and CCl_4.*		
		Vapor: I_2.	CCl_4 layer: Br_2. (Orange color shows BROMIDE.)	Water layer: Br_2, HCl, H_2SO_4. *Boil; then add $AgNO_3$.*
				Vapor: Br_2.	Precipitate: AgCl. (Shows CHLORIDE.)

Procedure 110. — *Detection of Thiocyanate and the Separate Halides.* — Transfer the $AgNO_3$ precipitate (P. 107) to a small casserole (see Note 1, P. 22); and treat it with 5 cc. of 15 n. NH_4OH. Add $(NH_4)_2S$ reagent, 10 drops at a time, till, after heating the mixture nearly to boiling and letting the precipitate settle, the reagent produces no further precipitate. Filter out and reject the precipitate.

Evaporate the filtrate till it no longer smells of ammonia, add 5 cc. of water, and filter out any precipitate. Pour the solution into a small separating funnel, add 1 cc. of HNO_3, 3–8 cc. of $Fe(NO_3)_3$ solution, and 1 cc. of CCl_4 (carbon tetrachloride), and shake the mixture for a minute or two. (Purple color of the carbon-tetrachloride layer, presence of IODIDE; red color of the aqueous layer, presence of THIOCYANATE or of much IODIDE.)

In case iodide is absent, proceed as described in the next to last paragraph of this Procedure.

In case iodide is present, draw off the CCl_4, add 3 cc. of fresh CCl_4, and shake the mixture; repeating these operations till the CCl_4 layer no longer has a dark purple color. (Red color in the aqueous layer, presence of THIOCYANATE.) Transfer the aqueous layer to a casserole, boil it for one minute, cool the mixture, pour it into a separating funnel, add 1 cc. of CCl_4, shake the mixture, and treat it as follows.

Add to the mixture in the separating funnel 2 cc. of HNO_3, and then 0.2 n. $KMnO_4$ solution, 2 drops at a time, till the aqueous layer becomes purple. (Yellow or orange color in the carbon-tetrachloride layer, presence of BROMIDE.)

Transfer the aqueous layer to a flask, dilute it to about 40 cc. with water; and, in case bromide or thiocyanate is present, boil the mixture for 5 minutes, adding more 0.2 n. $KMnO_4$ if the mixture loses its purple color (which should be pronounced enough to be noticeable even though a brown precipitate has separated). Add to the mixture 3 n. (chloride-free) $NaNO_2$ solution, 2–3 drops at a time, till the purple color disappears and any precipitate has dissolved. Then add 1–5 cc. of $AgNO_3$ solution. (White precipitate, presence of CHLORIDE.)

Notes. — 1. The $AgNO_3$ precipitate is treated first with NH_4OH, and not directly with $(NH_4)_2S$ reagent, because the NH_4OH dissolves the silver precipitate wholly or in part, and thus, by diminishing the extent to which the particles become coated with Ag_2S, makes the metathesizing action of the $(NH_4)_2S$ reagent more rapid. The use of NH_4OH also facilitates the manipulation, making it easier to remove the paper from the mixture.

2. The 5 cc. of 15 n. NH_4OH dissolves the maximum quantity of AgCl that may be present, but only a small quantity of AgSCN or AgBr, and scarcely any AgI. The behavior towards NH_4OH may therefore indicate the character of the halide present.

3. The greatly increased solubility of these silver salts in NH_4OH is due to the formation of complex silver-ammonia cations, of which $Ag(NH_3)_2^+$ is the one that is mainly produced, so long as the NH_4OH is only moderately concentrated; and under these conditions it can readily be shown, by combining the mass-action expression for the

dissociation of this complex ion with the solubility-product expression for the silver salt, that the solubility of a silver salt in NH_4OH solution is proportional to its solubility in water (provided this is small) and to the concentration of the NH_4OH.

4. That even so slightly soluble a substance as AgI is almost completely metathesized by $(NH_4)_2S$ is due to the extraordinarily small solubility of Ag_2S.

5. It is important to use nearly colorless $(NH_4)_2S$ reagent of standard concentration, which has not been decomposed by standing; for otherwise the large quantity of sulfur that separates during the evaporation and the reducing action of non-volatile sulfur acids present as impurities will interfere with the detection of the halides.

6. The fact that iodide is the only one of the three halides that reduces ferric salts (with liberation of the halogen) is due to the values of the molal reduction-potentials of the three halide ions in relation to that of ferrous ion. Thus by reference to the Table in the Appendix it is seen that Fe^{++}, Fe^{+++} has a smaller molal reduction-potential than I^-, I_2, but a much larger one than Br^-, Br_2, or Cl^-, Cl_2.

7. The addition of CCl_4 to the mixture serves the double purpose of making the test for iodide more delicate and characteristic, and of removing most of the free I_2 from the aqueous solution and thus enabling thiocyanate to be detected by the red color which it produces with ferric salts.

8. The quantity of I_2 or Br_2 that passes from the water layer into the CCl_4 layer is determined by the so-called distribution-law. According to this law, at any given temperature, after equilibrium is reached, a substance distributes itself between two non-miscible solvents in such proportions that the concentration of the substance in one solvent bears a definite ratio, called the distribution-ratio, to its concentration in the other solvent, whatever may be the relative quantities of the two solvents taken or the quantity of the substance originally present in either of them. The value of this ratio varies with the nature of the substance, the nature of the two solvents, and the temperature. At $25°$ its value for I_2 between carbon tetrachloride and water is 85; and its value for Br_2 between the same solvents is 23. This signifies that I_2 will pass into the CCl_4 layer from the water layer until its concentration (that is, the quantity of it per unit-volume) is 85 times as great in the CCl_4 layer as it is in the water layer; and that Br_2 will so pass till its concentration in the CCl_4 layer is 23 times as great as in the water layer.

9. The red color produced by ferric salts with thiocyanate is due to the formation of $Fe(SCN)_3$, which is less ionized than most salts of

the same valence type.   The color is pronounced even with 0.1–0.2 mg. of SCN; and the much less intense color produced by free I_2 will not be mistaken for it, provided this has been so far removed from the aqueous solution that the CCl_4 layer that has been shaken with it is pink, not a dark purple.

10. After the presence or absence of thiocyanate is determined, the remaining I_2 is expelled by boiling, since this removes it much more rapidly than continued extraction with CCl_4.   The mixture must not be boiled, however, before the presence or absence of thiocyanate has been determined, since $Fe(SCN)_3$ is decomposed by heating with I_2. The iodine must be completely removed, since even a small quantity would obscure the test for bromide.   The solution is shaken with a fresh portion of CCl_4 before the Br_2 is liberated by $KMnO_4$, to make sure that the solution is absolutely free from I_2.

11. In a cold moderately acid solution Br_2, but not Cl_2, is liberated by $KMnO_4$ from the corresponding halide.   This difference is not due, as is the different behavior of iodide and bromide toward ferric salts, to an intermediate value of the reduction-potential of the manganese compounds; for the value of this potential, though not well known, is in acid solution undoubtedly much smaller even than that of Cl^-, Cl_2.   The difference in this case arises primarily, not from difference in the equilibrium conditions, but from the fact that the rate of the reaction between $KMnO_4$ and bromide is very much greater than the rate of the reaction between $KMnO_4$ and chloride, at the same temperature and with the same concentrations of the reacting substances. Thus under the conditions prevailing when the $KMnO_4$ is first added, namely, at room temperature in a solution 1 n. to 1.5 n. in HNO_3, the rate of the bromide reaction is so large that most of the Br_2 is liberated almost immediately, while the rate of the chloride reaction is negligible.

12. The rate of both these reactions is very greatly increased by increase of temperature and by increase in the hydrogen-ion concentration.   Thus at the boiling temperature the rate of the chloride reaction would be fairly large in a solution 1 n. to 1.5 n. in HNO_3. Therefore, before the solution is boiled to expel the free Br_2, it is diluted to about 40 cc. with water, so as to reduce the hydrogen-ion concentration, and thus compensate the effect of the higher temperature. In the Procedure the HNO_3 concentration is so adjusted that even a small quantity of bromide is decomposed quickly in the cold, and only a small quantity of any chloride present is acted upon in the boiling solution.

13. The foregoing facts illustrate three general principles in regard to the rate of chemical reactions: first, that the rate, under given con-

ditions of temperature and concentration, varies within the widest possible limits with the nature of the chemical substances involved; second, that the rate with the same chemical substances at given concentrations increases very rapidly with rising temperature, 1000 fold as much time being often required to produce a given amount of change at 20° as at 100°; and third, that the rate with the same chemical substances at a given temperature is increased by increasing the concentration of any of the reacting substances, and in a higher degree for any substance of which a relatively large number of molecules are involved in the reaction. By writing the equation for the ionic reaction between bromide, permanganate, and any acid, 8 H^+ will be seen to react with 1 MnO_4^-, thus explaining the great effect of the concentration of the hydrogen-ion on the rate of the reaction.

14. Even $\frac{1}{3}$ mg. of bromide yields enough Br_2 to impart a noticeable yellow tinge to the 1 cc. of CCl_4. A small quantity of this solvent is used so as to increase the Br_2 concentration in it.

15. On boiling the mixture containing the $KMnO_4$ a brown precipitate of hydrated MnO_2 results when much bromide is present; for when, as in this case, a solution has only a moderate hydrogen-ion concentration, $HMnO_4$ may not be wholly converted by reducing substances to manganous salt, but may be partially reduced to the intermediate stage represented by the brown precipitate. On the subsequent addition of HNO_2 this substance, as well as any excess of $KMnO_4$, is instantaneously reduced and a colorless mixture results.

16. The presence of thiocyanate does not interfere with the test for chloride; for it is instantly destroyed (converted into sulfate) by the $KMnO_4$, before the $AgNO_3$ is added.

17. A small precipitate of $AgCl$ obtained at the end of the Procedure does not necessarily show the presence of chloride in the substance, unless the reagents have been proved to be entirely free from chloride. A blank test with the reagents should therefore be made in any doubtful case; and a turbidity should be compared with the precipitate produced by $\frac{1}{2}$ mg. of chloride, to determine whether it is really significant.

ANALYSIS OF THE SULFATE-GROUP.

TABLE XIX. — DETECTION OF SULFATE, SULFITE, CHROMATE, FLUORIDE, AND OXALATE.

Sodium Carbonate Solution Containing All Acidic Constituents. *Acidify with HCl, and add BaCl₂ (P. 111).*

Precipitate: BaSO₄. (Shows SULFATE.)	Filtrate: Na_2SO_3, $Na_2Cr_2O_7$, NaF, $Na_2C_2O_4$, $BaCl_2$. *Add Br_2.*		
	Precipitate: BaSO₄. (Shows SULFITE.)	Filtrate: $Na_2Cr_2O_7$, NaF, $Na_2C_2O_4$, $BaCl_2$. *Add NaAc and $CaCl_2$.*	
		Yellow precipitate: $BaCrO_4$ White precipitate: CaF_2, CaC_2O_4. *Treat portions as follows:*	
		Heat with SiO_2 and H_2SO_4 (P. 112).	*Dissolve in HNO_3, add $KMnO_4$, distil.*
		Gas: SiF_4. *Test with water.*	Vapors: CO_2. *Collect in $Ba(OH)_2$.*
		Turbidity: H_2SiO_3. (Shows FLUORIDE.)	Precipitate: $BaCO_3$. (Shows OXALATE.)

Procedure 111. — *Detection of Sulfate, Sulfite, Chromate, Fluoride, and Oxalate.* — In case in P. 103 BaCl₂ and CaCl₂ produced a precipitate, treat 6 cc. of the Na₂CO₃ solution (P. 101) as follows (first adding 2–10 cc. of AgNO₃ solution, shaking the mixture, and filtering out the precipitate, in case in P. 106 sulfide, or in P. 110 thiocyanate, was found present).

Slightly acidify the solution with HCl, adding it 10 drops at a time till the solution reddens litmus paper. Filter out and reject any precipitate. To the filtrate add just 1 cc. of HCl and 5 cc. of BaCl₂ solution, and let the mixture stand in the cold 2 or 3 minutes. (White precipitate, presence of SULFATE.) Filter out and reject the precipitate.

To the filtrate add at once saturated Br₂ solution, 1 cc. at a time, till the liquid after shaking smells of it, and heat the mixture nearly to boiling.   (White precipitate, presence of SULFITE.) Filter out and reject the precipitate.

To the filtrate add 10 cc. of 3 n. NaAc solution and 10 cc. of CaCl₂ solution, and let the mixture stand at least 15 minutes. (Yellow precipitate, presence of CHROMATE ; white precipitates presence of FLUORIDE or OXALATE.)   Shake the mixture vigorously so as to suspend the precipitate, and pour one-half of it through each of two filters.   Reject the filtrates.   Wash the precipitates thoroughly.

Treat one portion of the precipitate by P. 112, to determine the presence of fluoride.

Treat the other portion of the precipitate, to determine the presence of oxalate, as follows.   Pour repeatedly through the filter containing it a 5 cc. portion of hot HNO₃.   Arrange a distilling apparatus as described in the first paragraph of P. 117. Pour into the distilling flask through the safety-tube the HNO₃ solution, and also a 5 cc. portion of 0.2 n. KMnO₄ solution which has been previously acidified with HNO₃ and heated to boiling. Boil the contents of the flask for 2 or 3 minutes.   (White precipitate in the Ba(OH)₂ solution, presence of OXALATE.)

Notes. — 1. As to the solubilities of barium and calcium salts on which this method of analysis depends, see the Notes on P. 103.

2. AgNO₃ is added in case sulfide or thiocyanate is present in order to remove these constituents, which otherwise would be oxidized by the Br₂ with the formation of precipitates, namely, of S in the case of sulfide and of BaSO₄ in that of thiocyanate.

3. In the presence of the quantities of HAc and NaAc prescribed in the Procedure, BaCl₂ alone would yield a precipitate with fluoride only when more than 10 mg. of F is present, and with oxalate only when more than 5 mg. of C₂O₄ is present ; but CaCl₂ produces a cloudiness with ½ mg. of either of these constituents within 15 minutes.

4. The NaAc and CaCl₂ solutions used as reagents must be free from sulfate, since otherwise a precipitate of BaSO₄ will be obtained in the fluoride-oxalate test. These reagents should be tested in advance with BaCl₂ for this impurity ; and, if found present, it should be removed by adding a little BaCl₂ solution to the reagent, heating to boiling, and filtering.

5. Thiosulfate ($S_2O_3^=$) is a somewhat rare constituent of industrial products which, when treated by this Procedure, would, like sulfite, yield a precipitate of $BaSO_4$ on addition of Br_2 solution.   When present in considerable amount, it shows itself by producing a precipitate when the Na_2CO_3 solution is acidified with HCl, since it rapidly decomposes into sulfur and sulfite under the catalytic influence of a considerable concentration of hydrogen-ion.

Procedure 112. — *Confirmatory Test for Fluoride.* — Roll up the filter containing the $CaCl_2$ precipitate (P. 111), wind a platinum wire around it, and heat it till it is completely incinerated, allowing the ash to fall on to a watch-glass.   Mix intimately with the ash, or with a portion of it if it is large, 2 or 3 times its volume of finely powdered quartz (not artificially prepared silica) ; and transfer it with the aid of a piece of smooth paper to a dry test-tube, about 100 mm. in length and 12 mm. in bore.   Add from a dropper enough 95% H_2SO_4 to make a thin paste, taking care not to wet the sides of the tube.   Insert in the tube a somewhat narrower glass tube, wet on the inside but dry on the outside, so that it extends to within 3 cm. of the bottom, supporting it at the proper height by a rubber band or stopper.   Heat the mixture carefully over a small flame (not enough to vaporize the H_2SO_4) for a minute or two.   (White precipitate, in the wet part of the inner tube, presence of FLUORIDE.)

Notes. — 1. This confirmatory test depends on the fact that the HF liberated from the CaF_2 by the H_2SO_4 reacts with the SiO_2 with the formation of gaseous SiF_4, and on the fact that this gas on coming into contact with water reacts with it, precipitating H_2SiO_3 and leaving H_2SiF_6 (fluosilicic acid) in solution.

2. Great care must be used to have the test-tube and the materials perfectly dry, and concentrated (95%) H_2SO_4 must be employed; for otherwise the SiF_4 will be decomposed before it comes into contact with the wet walls of the inner tube.

3. The SiO_2 used should be in the form of powdered quartz, not of precipitated and ignited silicic acid; for the test is far less delicate with the latter material, since it retains much of the fluorine, apparently in the form of $SiOF_2$.

DETECTION OF OTHER CONSTITUENTS IN THE SODIUM CARBONATE SOLUTION

TABLE XX. — DETECTION OF NITRATE, NITRITE, BORATE, ARSENATE, AND ARSENITE.

Sodium Carbonate Solution Containing All the Acidic Constituents.
Treat portions as follows:

Boil with NaOH and Al (*P. 113*).	Add HAc and CSN$_2$H$_4$ (*P. 114*).		Add HCl, C$_2$H$_5$OH, and turmeric (*P. 115*).	Add HCl, NH$_4$OH, and Mg(NO$_3$)$_2$ (*P. 116*).	
Vapor: NH$_3$. *Test with* K$_2$HgI$_4$.	Gas: N$_2$.	Solution: NH$_4$SCN. *Add FeCl$_3$.*	Orange color. (Shows BORATE.)	Precipitate: MgNH$_4$AsO$_4$. *Treat with AgNO$_3$.*	Filtrate: NH$_4$AsO$_2$. *Pass in* H$_2$S.
Red precipitate: HgO·HgNH$_2$I. (Shows NITRATE or NITRITE.)		Red color: Fe(SCN)$_3$. *(Show NITRITE.)*		Red residue: Ag$_3$AsO$_4$. (Shows ARSENATE.)	Yellow precipitate, As$_2$S$_3$. (Shows ARSENITE.)

Procedure 113. — *Detection of Nitrate or Nitrite.* — In case in P. 104 oxidizing acidic constituents have been found present, place 2 cc. of the Na$_2$CO$_3$ solution (P. 101), 10 cc. of water, and 3 cc. of NaOH solution in a 50-cc. round-bottom flask. (See Note 4.) (In case in P. 91 ammonium was found present, boil the mixture till one-third of it has distilled off, and cool it.) Add to the mixture 1 cc. of aluminum turnings. Hold in the vapors a glass rod wet with K$_2$HgI$_4$ reagent, and heat the mixture gently so as to keep up a brisk evolution of hydrogen. (Orange or red precipitate on the rod, presence of NITRATE or NITRITE.) If a reddish precipitate forms, in order to estimate the quantity of nitrate or nitrite present, insert at once in the neck of the flask a rubber stopper fitted with a delivery-tube leading to the bottom of a test-tube containing 5 cc. of water placed in a beaker of cold water, and distil slowly till about one-

third of the liquid has passed over. To the distillate add K_2HgI_4 reagent, a few drops at a time, so long as the precipitate increases. (Orange or red precipitate, presence of NITRATE or NITRITE.)

Notes. — 1. Both nitrate and nitrite are reduced to NH_3 in alkaline solution by metals which evolve hydrogen. The NH_3 produced is driven out of the solution by boiling, and is tested for as in the Procedure for the detection of ammonium (P. 91), with which this nitrate-nitrite test may be combined if desired.

2. As to the composition of the K_2HgI_4 reagent and the precipitate produced by it with NH_3, see Notes 2 and 3, P. 91.

3. To estimate the quantity of nitrate or nitrite present, the precipitate produced by the K_2HgI_4 reagent may be compared with that produced by adding the reagent directly to known solutions of NH_4Cl, taking into account the fact that 1 mg. of NH_4 corresponds to about 3 mg. of NO_2 or NO_3.

4. Cyanide, ferro and ferricyanide, and thiocyanate also yield NH_3 when treated by this Procedure. In case in P. 106–110 any of these constituents was found present, the diluted Na_2CO_3 solution should be shaken with about 0.5 cc. of solid Ag_2CO_3 and the precipitate filtered out, before adding the NaOH solution.

Procedure 114. — *Detection of Nitrite.* — In case in P. 113 nitrate or nitrite is found present, pour 1 cc. of the Na_2CO_3 solution (P. 101) into a test-tube, and add gradually 1 cc. of HAc. (See Note 2.) Then add 1 cc. of a 10% solution of thiourea (CSN_2H_4), and let the mixture stand five minutes. (Formation of gas bubbles, indication of NITRITE.) Add 1 cc. of HCl and 1 cc. of $Fe(NO_3)_3$ solution. (Red color, presence of NITRITE; no red color, presence of NITRATE.)

Notes. — 1. The nitrite test is based on the following reaction which takes place in solutions with small hydrogen-ion concentrations:

$$CS(NH_2)_2 + HONO = N_2 + HSCN + 2 H_2O.$$

2. No other constituent gives rise to HSCN; but, in case thiocyanate or iodide is present in the substance, as shown in P. 110, it would produce a red color with $Fe(NO_3)_3$. In that case it must be removed by shaking the Na_2CO_3 solution with about 0.5 cc. of solid Ag_2CO_3 and filtering out the residue, before adding the HAc and thiourea.

3. No provision is made for the detection of nitrate in the presence of nitrite, since no satisfactory qualitative method is known.

Procedure 115. — *Detection of Borate.* — Add to just 3 cc. of the Na_2CO_3 solution (P. 101) just 8 cc. of 12 n. HCl, gradually at first; then add 8 cc. of ethyl alcohol, allow the salt to settle, and decant the solution into a test-tube. (See Note 3.) Add from a dropper just two drops of a solution of turmeric in ethyl alcohol, and let the mixture stand 10 minutes. (Orange or red color, presence of BORATE.) Compare the color with that of standards. (See Note 2.)

Notes. — 1. The red color which boric acid gives to turmeric is in high degree dependent upon the concentrations of the HCl, the alcohol, and the turmeric; and, to secure delicacy of the test and results that are comparable in different cases, the directions given must be closely adhered to; in which case $\frac{1}{2}$ mg. of BO_2 in the solution tested can be detected.

2. To make sure of the presence of borate when the color is slight, and to estimate the quantity present in other cases, the color should be compared with standards made by mixing 8 cc. of ethyl alcohol, 8 cc. of 12 n. HCl, and two drops of turmeric solution with 3 cc. of water (as a blank) or with 3 cc. portions of solutions containing known quantities of borate (for example, 1 mg. and 10 mg. of BO_2).

3. Chlorate, nitrite, and chromate, because of their strong oxidizing power, affect the color of the turmeric. Iodide may also be decomposed by the oxygen of the air, and the color of the I_2 liberated may obscure the borate test. Therefore, in case any of these constituents has been found present, evaporate 3 cc. of the Na_2CO_3 solution (P. 101) to dryness, add gradually 2 cc. of 12 n. HCl, and evaporate again to dryness. To the residue add 1 cc. of 3 n. Na_2CO_3 solution and 2 cc. of water; heat to boiling; filter if there is a residue; and treat the solution with reagents as directed in the Procedure. The evaporation with HCl serves to reduce the oxidizing substances and expel HI, and the addition of Na_2CO_3 precipitates any chromium that may be present. The solution is not ordinarily evaporated with HCl, when the absence of conflicting substances makes it unnecessary, since there is considerable loss of boric acid in evaporating acid solutions.

Procedure 116. — *Detection of Arsenate and Arsenite.* — In case in P. 44 arsenic was found present, dilute 5 cc. of the Na_2CO_3 solution (P. 101) with 10 cc. of water, and add HNO_3, 1 cc. at a time, till the mixture reddens litmus paper. Then add NH_4OH, a few drops at a time, till the mixture turns litmus paper blue, avoiding an excess.   Filter if there is a precipitate.   Add 10 cc. of $Mg(NO_3)_2$ reagent.   Let the mixture stand for 10 minutes, shaking it frequently.   (White precipitate, presence of ARSENATE or PHOSPHATE.)   Filter, and wash the precipitate with 1 n. NH_4OH.

To the filtrate add HCl, 1 cc. at a time, till it reddens litmus paper, and pass H_2S into the cold solution for about a minute. (Immediate yellow precipitate, presence of ARSENITE.)   (See Note 3.)

Pour on to the filter containing the $Mg(NO_3)_2$ precipitate 1 cc. of $AgNO_3$ solution to which a few drops of HAc have been added. (Dark-red residue, presence of ARSENATE.)   In case the residue is yellow, pour repeatedly through the filter containing it a 5 cc. portion of HCl, add to the solution 1 cc. of KI solution and 1 cc. of CCl_4, and shake the mixture.   (Purple color in the carbon-tetrachloride layer, presence of ARSENATE.)

Notes. — 1. This method of distinguishing arsenate and arsenite depends on the fact that arsenate is precipitated by $Mg(NO_3)_2$ reagent while arsenite is not. (See Notes 2 and 3, P. 44.) To prevent precipitation of magnesium arsenite, $Mg(AsO_3)_2$, however, the NH_4OH concentration must, as directed in this Procedure, be made as small as is consistent with securing complete precipitation of the arsenate. This precaution was not necessary in P. 44, where the arsenic is all in the form of arsenate and where the addition of a large quantity of NH_4OH serves to produce more rapid precipitation.

2. The characteristic dark-red color of the Ag_3AsO_4 produced by treatment of the $MgNH_4AsO_4$ with $AgNO_3$ solution (see Note 4, P. 44) is a sufficient confirmation of the presence of arsenate when phosphate is not present. Phosphate, however, is also precipitated by the $Mg(NO_3)_2$ reagent; and it is converted by the $AgNO_3$ into bright-yellow Ag_3PO_4. Moreover, in case a very large quantity of arsenite is present, it may be partially precipitated by the $Mg(NO_3)_2$ reagent; and it will then be converted into yellow Ag_3AsO_3 by $AgNO_3$. These yellow precipitates may obscure the color of a relatively small proportion of arsenate; and in this case the further confirmatory test with HCl and KI becomes necessary. In this test the production of a purple color shows the presence of arsenate; for I_2 is not liberated from iodide by either phosphate or arsenite.

M

3. The immediate formation of a yellow precipitate in the filtrate from the $Mg(NO_3)_2$ precipitate is a conclusive test for arsenite, except in case antimony is present in the substance. This element may pass into the Na_2CO_3 solution, and it then would yield a precipitate with H_2S, which might be mistaken for As_2S_3. Moreover, the arsenite test is sometimes obscured by other elements, especially copper, which may pass into the Na_2CO_3 solution and produce dark precipitates with H_2S. Hence, in case antimony is present, or in case the H_2S precipitate is not of the characteristic yellow color, it should be treated by P. 44, to determine whether arsenic is present in it.

4. Even if through faulty procedure a small quantity of arsenate passes into the filtrate from the $Mg(NO_3)_2$ precipitate, it will not yield an immediate precipitate with H_2S in the cold weakly acid solution (see Note 7, P. 21), and will therefore not lead to a mistaken conclusion as to the presence of arsenite.

DETECTION OF CARBONATE AND SULFIDE IN THE ORIGINAL
SUBSTANCE

Procedure 117. — *Detection of Carbonate and Sulfide by Distillation.* — Set up in the way shown in the figure an apparatus consisting of a 50-cc. round-bottom hard-glass flask fitted with a rubber stopper, through which pass a delivery-tube and a safety-tube, 20–30 cm. long, leading to the bottom of the flask. Hold the flask with a ring or clamp in an inclined position. Lead the end of the delivery-tube through a two-hole stopper into 25 cc. of nearly saturated $Ba(OH)_2$ solution contained in a 50-cc. flask supported in a beaker of cold water.

Place 0.5 g. of the very finely powdered substance and about 0.2 cc. of granulated Zn in the distilling flask. (See Note 2.) Boil in a small flask for about a minute a mixture of 5 cc.

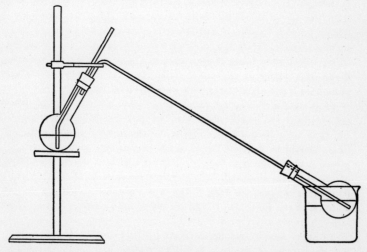

of water and 5 cc. of HCl, and pour it into the distilling flask with the aid of a small funnel connected temporarily with the safety-tube by means of rubber tubing. Heat the mixture slightly at first, then to boiling, and boil it gently till 2–3 cc. of liquid have distilled over.

To the distillate add HAc, 1 cc. at a time, till it reddens blue litmus paper. (White precipitate dissolving partly or com-

pletely on addition of the acid, presence of CARBONATE.) Add
to the mixture 5 cc. of PbAc₂ solution. (Black precipitate,
presence of SULFIDE.)

In case in P. 104, 110, or 111 oxidizing constituents or thiocyanate or sulfite were found present, transfer the residue undissolved by Na₂CO₃ solution (P. 101), with the filter-paper if
necessary, to a 50-cc. round-bottom flask, and treat it as described in the first two paragraphs of this Procedure, in order
to detect sulfide.

> *Notes.* — 1. On heating with HCl all carbonates are decomposed
> with evolution of CO₂. In order that the test for carbonate may be
> reliable, care must be taken to exclude the CO₂ of the air by boiling the
> acid in advance, by heating the mixture regularly so that no air sucks
> in through the safety-tube, and by keeping the Ba(OH)₂ solution away
> from the air so far as possible. Even with these precautions it is
> seldom possible to prevent the absorption of enough CO₂ to produce a
> slight turbidity. Care must also be taken to prevent any of the dis-
> tilling liquid from being thrown over mechanically into the receiving
> flask, since many of the non-volatile constituents, like sulfate and
> phosphate, yield precipitates with Ba(OH)₂ solution.
>
> 2. In case in P. 111 sulfite has been found present, the Zn should
> not be added, the liquid poured into the flask should consist of 5 cc. of
> 3% H₂O₂ solution and 5 cc. of HCl, and the test for sulfide in the dis-
> tillate should be omitted. For, in the presence of sulfite the test for
> sulfide is unreliable (see Note 5), and the test for carbonate would be
> obscured by the evolution of SO₂, which forms with Ba(OH)₂ a white
> precipitate insoluble in HAc. This last difficulty is removed by the
> addition of the H₂O₂, which oxidizes the sulfite to sulfate and prevents
> any SO₂ from passing over.
>
> 3. Many sulfides are decomposed by HCl with evolution of H₂S;
> but the sulfides of the copper and tin groups, and certain persulfides
> like pyrite, FeS₂, are not much acted upon by this acid alone. These
> are, however, decomposed, either completely or to a large extent, when
> Zn is also present, in virtue of its reducing action. The sulfides of
> arsenic are only slightly acted on by HCl and Zn; but, as they dis-
> solve in Na₂CO₃ solution, sulfide will be detected in P. 106 when they
> are present. As to the need of supplementing the test for sulfide made
> in P. 106 by one made with the original substance or with the residue
> insoluble in Na₂CO₃ solution, see Note 5. P. 101.

4. In case arsenic or antimony is present in the substance, arsine (AsH$_3$) or stibine (SbH$_3$) may be evolved upon heating the substance with Zn and HCl. As these gases are extremely poisonous and are not absorbed by the Ba(OH)$_2$ solution, the distillation should be carried out under a hood in case arsenic or antimony is present.

5. This test for sulfide may fail when chlorate, chromate, nitrate, nitrite, or sulfite is present with it, owing to destruction of the H$_2$S by these substances. It may, moreover, lead to the conclusion that sulfide is present when it is not, in case the substance contains sulfite or thiocyanate, since these constituents also yield H$_2$S with Zn and HCl. Hence, in case any of these conflicting constituents has been found present, a further test for sulfide is made upon the residue undissolved by Na$_2$CO$_3$ solution, as described in the last paragraph of this Procedure. This residue does not contain the conflicting constituents; for these pass completely into the Na$_2$CO$_3$ solution.

ANALYSIS OF NATURAL SUBSTANCES AND IGNEOUS PRODUCTS

TABLE XXI. — DETECTION OF SULFATE, CARBONATE, SULFIDE, AND CYANIDE.

Boil 0.5 g. of the substance with HCl and Zn, collecting the distillate in Ba(OH)$_2$ solution; filter the mixture left in the distilling flask (P. 121).

Filtrate from mixture in distilling flask. Add BaCl$_2$.	Distillate. Precipitate: BaCO$_3$. (Shows CARBONATE.) Solution: BaS, Ba(CN)$_2$.	
Precipitate: BaSO$_4$. (Shows SULFATE.)	To a part of the mixture add HAc and PbAc$_2$.	To the rest of the mixture add FeCl$_2$, boil, add HCl.
	Black precipitate: PbS. (Shows SULFIDE.)	Blue precipitate: Fe$_4$(FeCN$_6$)$_3$. (Shows CYANIDE.)

Procedure 121. — *Detection of Sulfate, Carbonate, Sulfide, and Cyanide.* — Treat 0.5 g. of the very finely powdered substance as described in the first two paragraphs of P. 117.

Pour the contents of the distilling flask on to a filter. Reject the residue. (See Note 1.) To the filtrate add 5 cc. of BaCl$_2$ solution. (White precipitate, presence of SULFATE.)

In case the substance is of natural origin, treat the whole distillate as described in the third paragraph of P. 117 (to detect CARBONATE and SULFIDE).

In case the substance is an igneous product, treat two-thirds of the distillate as described in the third paragraph of P. 117 (to detect CARBONATE and SULFIDE); and to the remaining third add 1 cc. of FeCl$_2$ solution, boil the mixture for a minute or two, and add HCl, 1 cc. at a time, till the solution becomes acid. (Blue precipitate, presence of CYANIDE.)

Notes. — 1. All sulfates except those of barium, strontium, and lead are very soluble or moderately soluble in dilute HCl; and that of lead is decomposed by Zn. Hence, only in case barium or strontium has been found present and the substance is not completely dissolved by dilute acid (as used in P. 2) is it necessary to test a natural substance or an igneous industrial product further for sulfate. This may be done by transferring from the filter to a casserole the residue from the treatment with Zn and HCl, boiling it for 5–10 minutes with 10 cc. of 3 n. Na_2CO_3 solution, filtering, acidifying the filtrate with HCl, and adding $BaCl_2$ solution.

2. As to the precautions to be observed in order to make the test for carbonate reliable, see Note 1, P. 117.

3. As to the action of HCl and Zn on sulfides and on compounds of arsenic and antimony, see Notes 3 and 4, P. 117. Constituents that interfere with the test for sulfide (see Note 5, P. 117) are not present in natural substances and igneous industrial products.

4. Cyanide is never present in natural substances, but is occasionally present in igneous products. The test for it is based upon the formation of $Ba_2Fe(CN)_6$ by the action of $Ba(CN)_2$ on the $Fe(OH)_2$ and upon the reaction which takes place upon acidification between this ferrocyanide and the ferric salt which has been produced by the oxygen of the air. As a result of these two reactions, ferric ferrocyanide (Prussian blue) is formed, which is only slightly soluble in dilute HCl.

TABLE XXII. — DETECTION OF CHLORIDE, FLUORIDE, AND BORATE.

Distil 1 g. of the substance, first (A) with H_2SO_4 alone,
then (B) with addition of CH_3OH (P. 122).

A. First distillate.		*B*. Second distillate: $B(OCH_3)_3$.
To a portion add $AgNO_3$.	*To the remainder add NaAc and $CaCl_2$.*	*Add HCl, C_2H_5OH, and turmeric.*
Precipitate: AgCl. (Shows CHLORIDE.)	Precipitate: CaF_2. (Shows FLUORIDE.) *Confirm by P. 112.*	Orange or red color. (Shows BORATE.)

Procedure 122. — *Detection of Chloride, Fluoride, and Borate.* — Place 1 g. of the very finely powdered substance in a 50-cc. round-bottom hard-glass flask. Pour into the flask 6 cc. of 18 n. H_2SO_4. Insert a stopper carrying a safety-tube and

delivery-tube, arranging the apparatus as described in P. 117 and as shown in the figure in that Procedure. Lead the end of the delivery-tube into a receiving flask containing 5 cc. of water, supported in a beaker of cold water. Distil the mixture till the acid becomes oily and the flask becomes filled with white fumes, removing the flame momentarily once or twice during the distillation to cause the liquid in the safety-tube to run down into the flask.

Boil the distillate for a minute or two, and filter it if it is turbid. To one-fourth of the solution add 2 cc. of HNO_3 and 1–3 cc. of $AgNO_3$ solution. (White precipitate, presence of CHLORIDE.) To the remainder of the solution add 5 cc. of 3 n. NaAc solution and 5 cc. of $CaCl_2$ solution, heat the mixture nearly to boiling, and let it stand 15 minutes. (White precipitate, presence of FLUORIDE.) Treat the precipitate by P. 112, to confirm the presence of fluoride.

After the distilling flask has cooled completely, pour into it gradually 8 cc. of pure methyl alcohol (CH_3OH), and mix the liquids by shaking. Distil off most of the alcohol into a receiving flask containing a mixture of 3 cc. of water and 8 cc. of 12 n. HCl, heating the sides of the distilling flask with a small flame to prevent bumping. Pour the distillate into a graduate, add enough ethyl alcohol to make the volume 20 cc., and then add from a dropper two drops of a solution of turmeric in ethyl alcohol. (Orange or red coloration, presence of BORATE.) Compare the color with that of standard solutions containing known quantities of borate.

Notes. — 1. The heating with concentrated H_2SO_4 liberates from almost all substances, except certain silicates, the HCl, HF, and HBO_2 corresponding to any chloride, fluoride, or borate present. The distillation must be continued until the acid fumes freely, so as to secure as strong a decomposing action as possible, so as to drive over into the distillate all of the liberated HF, and so as to leave the acid anhydrous for the subsequent borate test.

2. The distillate may, in addition to HCl and HF, contain H_2S, HCN, H_2CO_3, H_2SiO_3 (passing over as SiF_4), and S, all coming from the substance, as well as H_2SO_4 and H_2SO_3 arising from volatilization

or reduction of the H_2SO_4 added.   Any H_2S, HCN, or H_2SO_3 present is removed by boiling the solution before making the tests for chloride and fluoride, since otherwise these acids would produce precipitates in these tests.   Any H_2SiO_3 or S present is filtered out. H_2SO_4 will not pass over (unless the distillation is continued much too long) in quantity sufficient to yield a precipitate of $CaSO_4$, especially as this substance is much more soluble in the NaAc solution than it is in pure water.

3. As to the conditions for securing precipitation of a small quantity of fluoride see Note 1, P. 103.   As to the confirmatory test, see the Notes on P. 112.

4. In the presence of concentrated H_2SO_4 methyl alcohol reacts with boric acid to form methyl borate, $B(OCH_3)_3$, which is a very volatile liquid.   This is largely decomposed in the acid distillate with formation of boric acid.   In regard to the color test for borate and the comparison with standard solutions, see Notes 1 and 2, P. 115.

Procedure 123. — *Detection of Sulfate, Fluoride, Borate, and Silicate in Substances Not Decomposed by Acids.* — In case the residue from the treatment of the substance with HNO_3 and HCl by P. 2 and 3 has been fused with Na_2CO_3 by P. 7, treat one-half of the aqueous extract obtained in P. 7 as follows:

Evaporate two-thirds of the solution to a volume of about 6 cc., and treat it by P. 111–112, to detect sulfate and flouride.

Make one-third of the solution slightly acid with HCl, evaporate it to dryness, moisten the residue with HCl, evaporate again to dryness, and heat the residue at 100–130° till it is perfectly dry, keeping the casserole in motion over a small flame.   After cooling add just 6 cc. of 6 n. HCl and warm the mixture.   (Fine white residue, presence of SILICATE.)   Filter.   Treat the residue as described in the first two paragraphs of P. 5, to confirm the presence of silicate.   To the solution add just 5 cc. of 12 n. HCl, 8 cc. of C_2H_5OH, and two drops of a solution of turmeric in C_2H_5OH.   Decant the solution from any salt that has separated into a test-tube, and let it stand 10 minutes.   (Orange or red color, presence of BORATE.)

Notes. — 1. This Procedure serves to detect fluoride and borate in certain silicates and other natural or ignited substances which are not acted upon by hot concentrated H_2SO_4, as used in P. 122. Also in the case of substances not completely dissolved by the treatment with HNO_3 and HCl in P. 2 and 3, it provides, in case the residue has not been treated with HF in P. 5, for the detection of silicate; or, in case the residue has been so treated, it affords a more reliable and quantitative detection of that constituent. In such difficultly decomposable substances it also makes more certain the detection of sulfate.

2. This method of testing for these acidic constituents is prescribed in the Procedure only in the cases where the residue from the treatment with HNO_3 and HCl has been fused with Na_2CO_3 in accordance with the directions in P. 6 and 7. These directions require such fusion either when the residue could not conveniently be treated with HF, or when it has been so treated and is not completely decomposed by it. Yet, even when the substance is completely decomposed by the treatment with HF, it is possible that it may not be sufficiently acted on by hot concentrated H_2SO_4 to liberate the HF and HBO_2 from any fluoride and borate present. This case is hardly common enough to warrant making provision for it a part of the regular system of analysis; but to make absolutely certain that these constituents are not missed, the analyst must, whenever the substance leaves a residue after the treatment with HNO_3 and HCl, fuse that residue with Na_2CO_3, and treat the aqueous extract as described in this Procedure.

3. As to the detection of sulfate and fluoride see the Notes on P. 111 and 112; as to that of silicate, see Notes 6 and 7, P. 3, and Note 4, P. 5; as to that of borate, see Notes 1 and 2, P. 115.

APPENDIX

I. PREPARATION OF THE REAGENTS.

SOLUTIONS OF ACIDS

Acetic, 6 n.: Mix 350 cc. of 99.5% acid with 650 cc. of water.
Hydrochloric, 12 n.: Use the c. p. acid of commerce of s. g. 1.19.
Hydrochloric, 6 n.: Mix 12 n. HCl with an equal volume of water.
Hydrofluoric, 48%: Use the pure acid sold in ceresin bottles.
Nitric, 16 n.: Use the c. p. acid of commerce of s. g. 1.42.
Nitric, 6 n.: Mix 380 cc. of HNO_3 (s. g., 1.42) with 620 cc. of water.
Perchloric, 6 n.: Mix 650 cc. of 60% c. p. acid with 350 cc. of water.
Sulfuric, 95%: Use the c. p. acid of commerce of s. g. 1.84.
Sulfuric, 18 n.: Pour 465 cc. of 95% H_2SO_4 into 535 cc. of water.
Sulfuric, 6 n.: Pour 95% H_2SO_4 into five volumes of water.

SOLUTIONS OF BASES

Ammonium hydroxide, 15 n.: Use the c. p. product of s. g. 0.90.
Ammonium hydroxide, 6 n.: Mix 400 cc. of 15 n. NH_4OH with 600 cc. of water.
Barium hydroxide, 0.4 n. (approximately): Shake 60 g. of $Ba(OH)_2 \cdot 8 H_2O$ with 1000 cc. of water at room temperature, and decant or filter the solution.
Potassium hydroxide, 6 n.: Add to 350 g. of best c. p. KOH enough water to make the volume 1000 cc.
Sodium hydroxide, 6 n.: Add to 250 g. of NaOH "purified by alcohol" enough water to make the volume 1000 cc.

SOLUTIONS OF AMMONIUM SALTS

Acetate, 3 n.: Dissolve 250 g. of the solid salt in enough water to make the volume 1000 cc.
Carbonate, 6 n.: Dissolve 250 g. of freshly powdered ammonium carbonate in enough cold 6 n. NH_4OH to make the volume 1000 cc.
Chloride, 3 n.: Dissolve 160 g. of NH_4Cl in enough water to make the volume 1000 cc.
Molybdate, 1 n. in $(NH_4)_2MoO_4$, 3 n. in NH_4NO_3: Dissolve 90 g. of the pure ammonium molybdate of commerce ($(NH_4)_6Mo_7O_{24} \cdot 4H_2O$) in 100 cc. of 6 n. NH_4OH, add 240 g. of NH_4NO_3, and dilute the solution to 1000 cc.

Sulfide: Pass H_2S gas into 200 cc. of 15 n. NH_4OH in a bottle immersed in running water or in iced water till the gas is no longer absorbed; then add 200 cc. of 15 n. NH_4OH and enough water to make the volume 1000 cc.

SOLUTIONS OF OTHER SALTS

Dissolve the quantity given in the last column of the following table of each of the salts whose formula is given in the third column in enough water to make the volume 1000 cc.

Salt	Normal Concen.	Formula	Formula Weight	Grams per Liter
Barium chloride . . .	1	$BaCl_2 \cdot 2H_2O$	244	120
Calcium chloride* . . .	1	$CaCl_2 \cdot 6H_2O$	219	110
Cobalt nitrate	0.3	$Co(NO_3)_2 \cdot 6H_2O$	291	45
Ferric nitrate	1	$Fe(NO_3)_3 \cdot 9H_2O$	404	135
Lead acetate	1	$Pb(C_2H_3O_2)_2 \cdot 3H_2O$	379	190
Lead nitrate	1	$Pb(NO_3)_2$	331	165
Mercuric chloride . . .	0.2	$HgCl_2$	271	25
Nickel nitrate	1	$Ni(NO_3)_2 \cdot 6H_2O$	291	145
Potassium chromate . .	3	K_2CrO_4	194	290
Potassium ferricyanide .	1	$K_3Fe(CN)_6$	329	110
Potassium ferrocyanide .	1	$K_4Fe(CN)_6 \cdot 3H_2O$	422	105
Potassium iodide . . .	1	KI	166	166
Potassium nitrite . . .	6	KNO_2	85	500
Potassium oxalate . .	3	$K_2C_2O_4 \cdot H_2O$	184	280
Potassium permanganate	0.2	$KMnO_4$	158	32
Potassium thiocyanate .	1	$KSCN$	97	100
Silver nitrate	1	$AgNO_3$	170	170
Sodium acetate . .	3	$NaC_2H_3O_2 \cdot 3H_2O$	136	410
Sodium arsenite . . .	1	$NaAsO_2$	130	130
Sodium carbonate . . .	3	Na_2CO_3	106	160
Sodium nitrite‡ . . .	3	$NaNO_2$	69	210
Sodium phosphate . .	1	$Na_2HPO_4 \cdot 12H_2O$	358	120
Sodium sulfate	1	$Na_2SO_4 \cdot 10H_2O$	322	160
Sodium sulfite	1	$Na_2SO_3 \cdot 7H_2O$	252	125

* This reagent must be entirely free from sulfate. In case the only salt available contains sulfate, mix with the solution 1% of its volume of $BaCl_2$ reagent, let the mixture stand, and filter it; noting on the label that the reagent contains $BaCl_2$. And in that case prepare a separate reagent containing no $BaCl_2$, for use in P. 122.

‡ In case the salt contains any chloride, mix with the solution 1% of its volume of $AgNO_3$ solution, and filter the mixture after vigorous shaking. Note on the label that the reagent contains $AgNO_3$.

SPECIAL REAGENTS

Bromine, saturated solution: Shake liquid bromine with water, leaving a small excess of it in contact with the solution.

Dimethylglyoxime, 0.1 n.: Dissolve 12 g. of the solid in 1000 cc. of 95% C_2H_5OH.

Ferrous chloride, 1 n.: Dissolve 65 g. of $FeCl_2$ in enough 0.6 n. HCl to make the volume 1000 cc., and keep the solution in contact with iron nails.

Hydrogen peroxide, 3 per cent.

Magnesium ammonium nitrate, 1 n. in $Mg(NO_3)_2$, 3 n. in NH_4NO_3: Dissolve 130 g. of $Mg(NO_3)_2 \cdot 6 H_2O$ and 240 g. of NH_4NO_3 in water, add 35 cc. of 6 n. NH_4OH, and dilute to 1000 cc.

Manganous chloride: To 12 n. HCl add powdered $MnCl_2 \cdot 4 H_2O$ until after shaking it no longer dissolves.

Potassium mercuric iodide, 0.5 n. in K_2HgI_4, 3 n. in NaOH: Dissolve 115 g. of HgI_2 and 80 g. of KI in enough water to make the volume 500 cc.; add 500 cc. of 6 n. NaOH; and decant the solution from any precipitate that may form on standing. Keep this stock solution in the dark.

Potassium antimonate, 0.1 molal in KH_2SbO_4, 0.5 n. in KOH: Add 22 g. of the best commercial salt to 1000 cc. of boiling water, boil for a minute or two till nearly all the salt is dissolved, quickly cool the solution, add 35 cc. of 6 n. KOH solution, let the mixture stand overnight, and filter it.

Sodium cobaltinitrite, 0.3 n. in $Na_3Co(NO_2)_6$, 3 n. in $NaNO_2$, 1 n. in HAc: Dissolve 230 g. of $NaNO_2$ in 500 cc. of water, add 165 cc. of 6 n. HAc and 30 g. of $Co(NO_3)_2 \cdot 6 H_2O$, let the mixture stand overnight, filter or decant the solution, and dilute it to 1000 cc.

Sodium sulfide, 3 n. in Na_2S, 1 n. in Na_2S_2, 1 n. in NaOH: Dissolve 480 g. of $Na_2S \cdot 9 H_2O$ and 40 g. of NaOH in water, add 16 g. of sulfur, shake the mixture till the sulfur dissolves, and dilute it to 1000 cc.

Stannous chloride, 1 n. in $SnCl_2$, 2 n. in HCl: Dissolve 115 g. of $SnCl_2 \cdot 2 H_2O$ in 170 cc. of 12 n. HCl, dilute the solution to 1000 cc., and keep it in bottles containing granulated tin.

Thiourea: Dissolve 100 g. of thiourea in 1000 cc. of water.

Turmeric: Shake an excess of turmeric powder with 95% C_2H_5OH, and filter the mixture.

SOLID REAGENTS

Aluminum turnings.

Antimony powder.

Bismuth dioxide (sold also as sodium bismuthate).

Glass beads.

Iron powder.

Potassium chlorate (powder).

Quartz powder.

Potassium chloride.

Sodium nitrate.

Silver carbonate.

Sodium carbonate (anhydrous).

Sodium peroxide (in 4 oz. cans).

Tin (mossy).

Zinc (finely granulated).

SOLVENTS

Carbon tetrachloride.

Ethyl alcohol (95%).

Ethyl alcohol (99%).

Methyl alcohol (acetone-free).

II. PREPARATION OF THE TEST–SOLUTIONS.

Of the powdered salt whose formula is given in the middle column of the following table weigh out the number of grams given in the last column, and add enough hot water (or acid when so stated in the footnote) to make the volume one liter. To prepare the test-solutions, which contain 10 mg. of the constituent per cubic centimeter, dilute these stock solutions, which contain 100 mg. of the constituent per cubic centimeter, with nine times their volume of distilled water. In a few cases (indicated by the letter H) where the substance is not sufficiently soluble, the stock solution is made up so as to contain 50 mg. of the constituent per cubic centimeter and must be diluted with four times its volume of water to yield the test-solution.— Since these solutions serve also for the preparation of the "unknown solutions," the purest salts that can be purchased should be employed.

Constituent	Formula of Salt	Grams per Liter	Constituent	Formula of Salt	Grams per Liter
Ag	$AgNO_3$	160	Zn	$Zn(NO_3)_2$	290
Pb	$Pb(NO_3)_2$	160	Cr	$Cr(NO_3)_3$	460
Hg(ous)	$Hg_2(NO_3)_2 \cdot 2H_2O$	140 (a)	Fe(ous)	$FeCl_2$	230 (f)
Bi	$Bi(NO_3)_3 \cdot 5H_2O$	230 (b)	Fe(ic)	$Fe(NO_3)_3 \cdot 9H_2O$	715
Cu	$Cu(NO_3)_2 \cdot 3H_2O$	380	Mn	$Mn(NO_3)_2 \cdot 6H_2O$	530
Cd	$Cd(NO_3)_2 \cdot 4H_2O$	275	Ni	$Ni(NO_3)_2 \cdot 6H_2O$	500
Hg(ic)	$HgCl_2$	65H	Co	$Co(NO_3)_2 \cdot 6H_2O$	500
As(ous)	As_2O_3	13 (c)	Ba	$BaCl_2 \cdot 2H_2O$	180
As(ic)	As_2O_5	150	Sr	$Sr(NO_3)_2$	240
Sb	$SbCl_3$	190 (d)	Ca	$Ca(NO_3)_2 \cdot 4H_2O$	590
Sn(ous)	$SnCl_2 \cdot 2H_2O$	190 (e)	Mg	$Mg(NO_3)_2 \cdot 6H_2O$	530H
Sn(ic)	$SnCl_4 \cdot 3H_2O$	270 (e)	Na	$NaNO_3$	370
Al	$Al(NO_3)_3 \cdot 9H_2O$	700H	K	KNO_3	260
S	$Na_2S \cdot 9H_2O$	375H	CrO_4	K_2CrO_4	170
CN	$NaCN$	190	F	KF	305
$Fe(CN)_6^{IV}$	$K_4Fe(CN)_6 \cdot 3H_2O$	210	C_2O_4	$K_2C_2O_4 \cdot H_2O$	210
$Fe(CN)_6^{III}$	$K_3Fe(CN)_6$	155	NO_3	$NaNO_3$	140
SCN	$KSCN$	170	NO_2	$NaNO_2$	150
I	KI	130	BO_2	$Na_2B_4O_7 \cdot 10H_2O$	90
Br	KBr	150	AsO_4	As_2O_5	85
Cl	$NaCl$	165	AsO_2	$Na_4As_2O_5$	150
ClO_3	$NaClO_3$	130	PO_4	$Na_2HPO_4 \cdot 12H_2O$	190H
SO_4	$Na_2SO_4 \cdot 10H_2O$	340	PO_4	$Ca_3(PO_4)_2$	160 (b)
SO_3	$Na_2SO_3 \cdot 7H_2O$	315			

(a) Dissolve in 0.6 n. HNO_3.   (b) Dissolve in 3 n. HNO_3.
(c) Digest with 500 cc. of 12 n. HCl; then add 500 cc. of water, yielding the test-solution of $AsCl_3$, containing 10 mg. of As per cubic centimeter.
(d) Dissolve in 6 n. HCl; and, in making the test-solution, dilute with 2 n. HCl.
(e) Dissolve in 6 n. HCl.   (f) Dissolve in 0.6 n. HCl, and keep in contact with iron nails

UNKNOWN SOLUTIONS

The "unknown solutions" given to the student should contain the constituents to be tested for in quantities which are definitely known by the instructor. As a rule they may well contain in 10 cc. 300 mg. of one of the constituents, 30 mg. of another of the constituents, and 3 mg. of each of two or three of the remaining constituents of the group in question. Such solutions may be conveniently prepared in advance by mixing in a 250 cc. bottle 60 cc. of the stock solution of the first constituent (or 120 cc. if it is half-strength as shown by an H in the table), 6 cc. of the stock solution of the second constituent (or 12 cc. if half-strength), and 6 cc. of the test-solutions of the other constituents, and diluting with enough water to make the volume 200 cc. Of these "unknown solutions" just 10 cc. should be given out to each student for analysis. When time permits the analysis of two unknown solutions in any group, the second may well contain only 2 mg. of some of the constituents.

SOLID TEST SUBSTANCES

Bleaching powder.	FeS_2 (pyrite).
$CaCO_3$ (powdered).	Fe_3O_4 (magnetite).
$Ca_3(PO_4)_2$ (powdered).	$NaC_2H_3O_2$.
$Cu(NO_3)_2 \cdot 3 H_2O$.	NH_4Cl.

Mixture of $BiOCl$ (30%), $Fe_2(SO_4)_3$ (30%), $NaNO_3$ (30%), $Na_2SO_3 \cdot 7 H_2O$ (10%).

Mixture of $CaSO_4 \cdot 2 H_2O$ (60%), $CaCO_3$ (20%), FeS_2 (10%), KCN (10%).

Mixture of CaF_2 (5%), $Na_2B_4O_7 \cdot 10 H_2O$ (5%), $NaCl$ (5%), sand (85%).

III. APPARATUS REQUIRED.

Returnable

2 Beakers, lipped, 150 and 400 cc.
2 Burners (Tirrill).
2 Casseroles, 30 cc.
2 Casseroles, 75 cc.
2 Casseroles, 150 cc.
2 squares Cobalt glass.
1 Crucible, nickel, 30 cc.
1 Filter-flask, conical, 500 cc., with a one-hole rubber stopper.
1 Flask, conical, 50 cc.
4 Flasks, conical, 100 cc., with 1 two-hole rubber stopper.
2 Flasks, conical, 200 cc., with 1 two-hole rubber stopper.
1 Flask, conical, 500 cc.
2 Flasks, round-bottom, 50 cc., with 1 two-hole rubber stopper.
1 Flask, flat-bottom, 250 cc., with a two-hole rubber stopper.
1 Flask, ring-neck, flat-bottom, 750 cc., with a two-hole rubber stopper.
1 Funnel, 50 mm.
3 Funnels, 65 mm.
1 Funnel support for 4 funnels.
1 Graduate, 10 cc.
1 Graduate, 50 cc.
1 Key for desk.
1 Mortar, porcelain, 80 mm.
1 Ring-stand with 3 rings.
1 Separating funnel, 50 cc.
6 Test-tubes, 100×12 mm.
12 Test-tubes, 150×18 mm.
2 Test-tubes, hard glass, 100×10 mm.
1 Test-tube rack.
1 Thistle-tube, 250 mm.
1 Triangle, nichrome, 50 mm.
4 Watch glasses, 40 mm.
2 Watch glasses, 75 mm.
2 Watch glasses, 100 mm.
1 Wing-top for burner.

Not Returnable

100 Filters, 7 cm., in filter box.
100 Filters, 9 cm., in filter box.
12 Filters, hardened, 5 cm.
12 Filters, hardened, 9 cm.
75 cm. Glass rod, 5 mm. diam.
150 cm. Glass tubing, 6 mm. outer diam.
150 cm. Glass tubing, 7 mm. outer diam.
1 box Labels.
1 tube Litmus paper, blue.
1 tube Litmus paper, red.
1 box Matches.
1 Note-book.
10 cm. Platinum wire.
2 Rubber nipples.
150 cm. Rubber tubing, bore 8 mm., wall 1.5 mm.
75 cm. Rubber tubing, bore 8 mm., wall 2 mm.
30 cm. Rubber tubing, pure, bore 5 mm.
1 Sponge.
1 Spoon, horn, bowl 1 cm. long.
1 Test-tube brush.
2 Towels.
2 Wire gauzes, 12×12 cm.

IV SOLUBILITIES.

GENERAL STATEMENT

Ammonium, potassium, and sodium salts: all very soluble in water.

Bismuth, antimony, tin, and mercury salts: all hydrolyzed by water with precipitation of the hydroxide or basic salt, but most of them very soluble in 1 n. HCl or HNO$_3$.

Nitrates, nitrites, and chlorates: all very soluble in water (except AgNO$_2$).

Carbonates, sulfites, borates, oxalates, phosphates, arsenates, and arsenites: all, except those of the alkali elements, slightly soluble in water, but very soluble in 1 n. HCl or HNO$_3$ (except Sn$_3$(PO$_4$)$_4$ and Sn$_3$(AsO$_4$)$_4$, which are very slightly dissolved even by concentrated HNO$_3$).

Hydroxides: all, except those of arsenic and the alkali elements, very slightly soluble in water (except also those of barium, strontium, and calcium, which are moderately soluble as shown in the following table); but all very soluble in 1 n. HCl or HNO$_3$ (except those of antimony and tin, which do not dissolve in HNO$_3$).

Chlorides, bromides, iodides, thiocyanates, and sulfates: all very soluble in water, except as shown in the following table and except the mercurous halides and HgI$_2$.

Cyanides, ferro and ferricyanides: very slightly soluble in water, except those of the alkali and alkaline-earth group, and except Hg(CN)$_2$.

Sulfides of the silver-, copper-, and tin-groups: all very slightly soluble in water and in cold 1 n. HCl or HNO$_3$.

Sulfides of the iron-group and of zinc: all very slightly soluble in water, but soluble in 1 n. HCl or HNO$_3$ (except FeS$_2$, NiS, and CoS).

Sulfides of the other elements: very soluble in water, or decomposed with separation of the hydroxide when this is insoluble.

SALTS OF THE ALKALINE-EARTH AND SILVER GROUPS

The numbers in the table show the solubility in milli-equivalents per liter at 20°. The letters v.s. (very soluble) denote a greater solubility than 1 normal. In the case of the carbonates the values have been corrected for hydrolysis so as to correspond to the ion-concentration product in the saturated solution.

	Mg	Ca	Sr	Ba	Pb	Ag
Chloride	v.s.	v.s.	v.s.	v.s.	70.	0.0100
Bromide	v.s.	v.s.	v.s.	v.s.	45.	0.0005
Iodide	v.s.	v.s.	v.s.	v.s.	2.6	0.00002
Thiocyanate	v.s.	v.s.	v.s.	v.s.	28.	0.0008
Sulfide	v.s.	v.s.	v.s.	v.s.	$0.0_{10}4$	$0.0_{14}7$
Sulfate	v.s.	30.	1.5	0.02	0.28	50.
Chromate	v.s.	60.	12.	0.03	0.0003	0.16
Carbonate	20.	0.2	0.2	0.2	0.0004	0.2
Hydroxide	0.3	45.	130.	450.	0.2	0.18
Fluoride	2.8	0.4	1.9	18.	5.	v.s.
Oxalate	5.	0.09	0.5	0.8	0.012	0.24

In KSp ena moles rather than equivalents.

V. IONIZATION VALUES.

The following table shows approximately the percentage of the substance which is dissociated into its ions in 0.1 normal solution at 25°. In the case of the dibasic and tribasic acids the value opposite the formula of the acid shows the percentage of the first hydrogen that is dissociated, and that opposite the acid ion (HA⁻) shows the percentage of it dissociated into H⁺ and A⁼ for the case that these two ions are present in equal quantities. In the case of the salts and very largely ionized acids and bases, the values given merely indicate roughly the magnitude of the mass-action effects exerted by their univalent ions; for much uncertainty still exists as to the true ionization of these substances.

Salts of type B^+A^- (*e.g.* KNO_3)	84%
Salts of type $B^+_2A^=$ or $B^{++}A^-_2$ (*e.g.* K_2SO_4 or $BaCl_2$)	73
Salts of type $B^+_3A^=$ or $B^{+++}A^-_3$ (*e.g.* $K_3Fe(CN)_6$ or $AlCl_3$) . . .	65
Salts of type $B^{++}A^=$ (*e.g.* $MgSO_4$)	40
KOH, NaOH	90
$Ba(OH)_2$	80
NH_4OH	1
HCl, HBr, HI, HSCN, HNO_3, $HClO_3$, $HClO_4$	90
H_2SO_4, H_2CrO_4, $H_4Fe(CN)_6$, $H_3Fe(CN)_6$	90
H_3PO_4, H_3AsO_4, H_2SO_3, $H_2C_2O_4$, HSO_4^-	20–40
HNO_2, HF	7–9
HAc, $HC_2O_4^-$, HSO_3^-	1–2
H_2S, H_2CO_3, $H_2PO_4^-$, $H_2AsO_4^-$, $HCrO_4^-$	0.1–0.2
HBO_2, $HAsO_2$, HCN, HCO_3^-, HClO	0.002–0.008
HS^-, $HPO_4^=$, $HAsO_4^=$	0.0001–0.0002
HOH	0.00,000,02

VI. MOLAL REDUCTION-POTENTIALS.

The following values are those of the actual reduction-potentials in volts for the case that the concentrations of the ions involved are 1 molal. They are referred to the potential of hydrogen gas at a pressure of one atmosphere against hydrogen-ion at 1 molal, taken as zero.

To find the actual potential for other concentrations add to these values for each tenfold decrease in the concentration of any ion present in the oxidized state 0.06, 0.03, or 0.02 respectively, according as the difference in valence in the two states is unity, two, or three, respectively; and subtract the same quantities from the given values for each tenfold decrease in the concentration of any ion present in the reduced state. In cases where only $\frac{1}{2}$ mol. of an ion or other dissolved substance (like $\frac{1}{2}$ Hg_2^{++} or $\frac{1}{2}$ Cl_2) is present in the oxidized (or reduced) state, add (or subtract) only one-half of these quantities for each tenfold decrease in its concentration.

Reduced State	Oxidized State	Reduction-Potential	Reduced State	Oxidized State	Reduction-Potential
K	K$^+$	2.92	Bi	Bi^{+++}	-0.30
Na	Na$^+$	2.71	Cu	Cu^{++}	-0.34
Zn	Zn^{++}	0.76	I$^-$	$\frac{1}{2}$I$_2$ (solid)	-0.54
Fe	Fe^{++}	0.44	Fe^{++}	Fe^{+++}	-0.75
Cd	Cd^{++}	0.40	Ag	Ag$^+$	-0.80
Sn	Sn^{++}	0.14	Hg	$\frac{1}{2}$(Hg$_2$)$^{++}$	-0.80†
Pb	Pb^{++}	0.12	$\frac{1}{2}$(Hg$_2$)$^{++}$	Hg^{++}	-0.92†
$\frac{1}{2}$H$_2$	H$^+$	0.00	Br$^-$	$\frac{1}{2}$Br$_2$(1 m.)	-1.10
Sb	Sb^{+++}	-0.20*	Cl$^-$	$\frac{1}{2}$Cl$_2$(1 m.)	-1.39
Sn^{++}	Sn^{++++}	-0.14*			

*These starred values denote the reduction-potentials for the (unknown) concentrations of the ions which prevail in solutions 1 molal in SbCl$_3$, SnCl$_2$, and H$_2$SnCl$_6$ in the presence of 1 normal HCl. The reduction-potentials cannot be given for 1-molal concentration of the respective ions, since the degrees of ionization and complex-formation in antimony and tin chloride solutions are imperfectly known.

† The values of the actual potentials of these two mercury combinations are -0.27 and -0.63, respectively, in the presence of 1 n. Cl$^-$ ion, owing to the very small solubility of Hg$_2$Cl$_2$ and the small ionization of HgCl$_2$.

VII. ATOMIC WEIGHTS OF THE COMMON ELEMENTS.

Aluminum	Al	27.0	Iron . . . . . . Fe 55.84
Antimony	Sb	120.2	Lead . . . . . . Pb 207.20
Arsenic	As	74.96	Magnesium . . . Mg 24.32
Barium	Ba	137.37	Manganese . . . Mn 54.93
Bismuth	Bi	209.0	Mercury . . . . Hg 200.6
Boron	B	10.9	Molybdenum . . Mo 96.0
Bromine	Br	79.92	Nickel . . . . . Ni 58.68
Cadmium	Cd	112.40	Nitrogen . . . . N 14.008
Calcium	Ca	40.07	Oxygen . . . . O 16.00
Carbon	C	12.005	Phosphorus . . . P 31.04
Chlorine	Cl	35.46	Potassium . . . K 39.10
Chromium	Cr	52.0	Silicon . . . . . Si 28.1
Cobalt	Co	58.97	Silver . . . . . Ag 107.88
Copper	Cu	63.57	Sodium . . . . Na 23.00
Fluorine	F	19.0	Strontium . . . Sr 87.63
Gold	Au	197.2	Sulfur . . . . . S 32.06
Hydrogen	H	1.008	Tin . . . . . . Sn 118.7
Iodine	I	126.92	Zinc . . . . . . Zn 65.37

INDEX

In this index the figures in black-face type refer to the Procedures and the figures after them in ordinary type refer to the Notes. Figures in italics preceded by the letter *p* refer to page numbers.